Lower Plants

Anatomy and Activities of Non-flowering Plants
and their Allies

C. J. Clegg

John Murray

Preface

This book is a concise, largely pictorial account of the complete range of lower plants and their allies studied at Advanced Level and similar courses (TEC Biology II and Cell Biology III). Structural, physiological, biochemical and ecological aspects are covered, along with essential features of taxonomy, reproduction and life-cycle.

I define the lower plants in the widest sense, as all those organisms that botanists have studied other than the angiosperms (angiosperms have received similar treatment in the companion book, *Anatomy and Activities of Plants: a guide to the study of Flowering Plants*, John Murray, 1980). For two or three decades, Advanced Level students have known that fungi were best seen as a separate kingdom, fundamentally different from both plants and animals. More recently we have also learnt to see bacteria and blue-green algae as separate kingdoms and levels of organisation. However, knowledge of these groups is a vital element in our understanding of biology as a whole, so these groups are dealt with here along with the true lower plants.

The great diversity of living things is acknowledged here by considering each organism in the context of the group of organisms that each was chosen to represent. In addition, the major principles of biology that have been observed in and experimented on with particular lower organisms are discussed. For example, our knowledge of photosynthesis in higher plants is based largely on studies of unicellular green algae. Similarly, in ecology, genetics and aspects of biochemistry, lower organisms have been widely used as experimental organisms. Many of the developments in biotechnology are centred on work with prokaryotes, with fungi and with certain smaller eukaryotes. The economic significance of lower plants in industry, in energy studies and in the search for alternative food sources is also given appropriate attention. This economic importance of lower plants and the delightful diversity of structure and function they show will, I hope, be communicated to a new generation of students by the combination of drawings, photographs and text employed in this book.

Acknowledgements

I am most grateful to all who have helped in the preparation of this book. I am particularly indebted to Mr Don Mackean (Welwyn Garden City) and Dr Richard Johnson (Aberdeen University) who painstakingly read the manuscript, and commented, corrected and advised on content, style and presentation. I have also had most helpful advice from Dr Alfred Keys of Rothamsted Experimental Station and Dr David Whitehouse of North East London Polytechnic on specific aspects of biochemistry. However, any remaining errors are my sole responsibility.

All the drawings are my own with the exception of four, found on pages 21, 87 and 88, provided by Judith, Sarah and Paul Clegg. The photographs, obtained from various sources, are credited individually. Various individuals and publishers gave permission to publish or adapt copyright materials, and these instances are acknowledged in the text. David Jeffrey, Lynn Hodgkinson, Yvonne Jones and Eugene Bucknor of the Science Section, Avery Hill College, provided the data on the effects of heavy metal ions on the growth of *Chlorella*, given on page 23. Dr. John Cowan of the Biology Department, King's College, University of London, supplied the samples of *Frullaria tamarisci* used in Figure 7.6. To all the unknown experimenters, observers, teachers and writers who have influenced my own understanding I gladly acknowledge my debt.

At John Murray, the skill and patience of Trevor Dolby and Trisha Groves have brought together text, drawings, annotations and photographs as I have wished, and I am most grateful to them.

CJC
1984

Safety note

Any experiments involving the use of micro-organisms may be potentially hazardous. They should be carried out under close supervision, following the advice given in *Safeguards in the School Laboratory*, available from The Association for Science Education, College Lane, Hatfield, Hertfordshire AL10 9AA.

Other Books by the same author

Anatomy and Activities of Plants (with Gene Cox)
Test Your Biology: Questions and Answers (with A. E. Pound)

First published 1984
by John Murray (Publishers) Ltd
50 Albemarle Street, London W1X 4BD

Typeset, printed and bound in Great Britain
by Fletcher & Son, Ltd, Norwich

British Library Cataloguing in Publication Data

Clegg, C. J.
Lower plants: anatomy and activities of
non-flowering plants and their allies.
I. Plants
I. Title
586   QK45.2

ISBN 0-7195-4010-0

Contents

The range of plant life and its classification

1. Classification: its need and role

There are more than one and a half million different types of organisms known and their numbers are continually being added to as a result of new studies. We classify them in order to provide a general plan of the immense diversity of form that exists. Classification aims to use as many characteristics as possible in placing similar organisms together and dissimilar ones apart. Classification is not rigid. It is an artificial creation on the best available evidence using limited knowledge, to reflect fundamental relationships. Classification is on the basis of:

(a) levels of organisation,

(b) evolutionary relationships, although these are known very imperfectly.

As the classification is refined so the more it reflects relationships.

Classification is of great importance in biology because:

(a) it enables communication to occur. Studies cannot be compared unless they are known to refer to exactly the same types of organism,

(b) it enables biologists to make generalisations (and it provides a basis for prediction) about the possible origins, the major role, the usefulness and the consequences of various structures, life-styles and feeding relationships.

In short, classification facilitates biology. The science of classification is known as taxonomy. Classification is standardised throughout the world as a result of the International Code of Botanical Nomenclature (and through the corresponding work of the International Committee on Zoological Nomenclature).

2. Classification: the system

The accepted scheme of classification has been developed from the work of Carl Linnaeus (1707–78), a naturalist who created the binomial system of nomenclature, popularly adopted from 1758. Every species of plant (and animal) is given two Latinised names, e.g. *Ranunculus acris* (Common Buttercup), *Homo sapiens* (Man). The specific or trivial name comes second and follows the generic name which is shared with other related species considered to be sufficiently similar to be grouped in the same genus, e.g. *Ranunculus repens* (Creeping Buttercup). The whole scheme of classification is hierarchical. Above the species level, organisms are placed in wider groupings; the higher the category the more diverse species are included.

Kingdom	the largest and most inclusive group, e.g. plants and animals
Division/ (phylum)	organisms constructed on a similar, general plan and thought to be related, e.g. vascular plants (tracheophytes)
Class	a group within a phylum, e.g. ferns (Filicinae)
Order	a group of apparently related families, e.g. Filicales
Family	a group of apparently related genera, e.g. Polypodiaceae
Genus	a group of similar and closely related species, e.g. *Pteridium*
Species	a group of interbreeding individuals not interbreeding with another such group. A species may include 'races' or 'varieties'. Species have two names, one generic, the other specific, e.g. *Pteridium aquilinum*

There is no uniformity in the size of the categories; a group may contain one or many hundred.

Living things

Prokaryotic organisms
Blue-green algae, bacteria. The electron microscope has helped show:

(i) cell has no distinct nucleus although it contains DNA,

(ii) lacks mitochondria, chloroplasts and complex structured flagella,

(iii) cell wall of distinct composition and containing mucopeptides (of protein origin).

Viruses
Agents of disease that require to be transmitted from host to host. They are not 'alive' outside the host cell. Most viruses are constructed from protein and nucleic acid alone. Viruses are only capable of replication within specific host cells.

Eukaryotic organisms
Plants, animals, fungi, i.e. the majority of living things. The electron microscope has helped show:

(i) cell has nucleus separated from the cytoplasm by its nuclear membrane,

(ii) cytoplasm compartmentalised by membranes into regions called organelles, e.g. endoplasmic reticulum, mitochondria and chloroplasts,

(iii) eukaryotic flagella and cilia are made of a series of tubes arranged in a cylindrical manner,

(iv) cell wall (when present) is usually made of cellulose.

3. Fundamental differences: animals and plants – are there other kingdoms?

Living things have traditionally been classified as animals or plants. Today the eukaryotes (see below) are now divided into three kingdoms:

kingdom of animals, kingdom of plants, kingdom of fungi.

Fungi resemble plants in that, with few exceptions, they have definite cell walls, are usually non-motile (although they may have motile reproductive cells) and they reproduce by spores. Fungi differ from green plants in that they lack chlorophyll, and their cell walls may contain chitin rather than cellulose.

Figure 1.1 The diversity of living things summarised in a matrix contrasting the principle modes of nutrition with levels of organisation

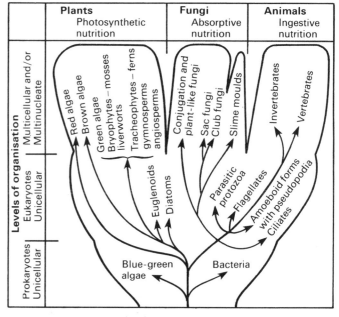

Adapted from R. Whittaker's *Five Kingdom System* and G. Leedales *Four Kingdom System* as presented by M. Tribe, A. Morgan and P. Whittaker in *The Evolution of Eukaryotic Cells*, Arnold Studies in Biology (131) 1981

4. Prokaryotic and eukaryotic organisation

The development of electron microscopy has led to the discovery of two types of cellular organisation, the smaller, simpler prokaryotic cell, and the more complex eukaryotic cell. In addition there are viruses. These are structurally simpler (see page 15), for they contain protein and nucleic acid only, and are unable to multiply outside host cells. It is questionable whether viruses can be recognised as living things.

The electron microscope

The transmission electron microscope employs electrons to produce a magnified image in a similar way to the optical microscope's use of light. Electrons from an electron gun are focused by varying the current passing through circular electromagnetic lenses. The image must be observed on a fluorescent screen because the human eye is not sensitive to electrons as it is to light. A permanent record of the image is made on a photographic plate. Electrons are easily scattered in collision with other atoms, so air must be removed from the path of the electrons, and the inside of the electron microscope is maintained at a very low pressure ('vacuum'). Consequently living or wet specimens cannot be examined, except under very special circumstances. The specimens must be relatively thin with membranes or other structures stained with chemicals that scatter electrons.

An alternative form of electron microscope, the scanning electron microscope, produces an image from electrons reflected from the surface of the specimen. This usually has a lower resolution than the transmission electron microscope, but a relatively immense depth of field which permits the structure of the surface of solid objects to be observed in focus. The fineness of detail which may be made out is a measure of the resolving power or resolution of a microscope, whereas the magnification tells us about the size of the image (but not the amount of detail). The electron microscope achieves greater resolution than the light microscope and therefore enables greater useful magnification.

Figure 1.2 A comparison of the transmission electron microscope and light microscope

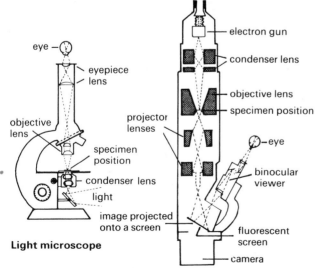

Light microscope / Transmission electron microscope

The lenses of the electron microscope are electromagnetic coils that focus the electron beam (negatively charged particles) by the magnetic field they produce. The current passing through the lenses may be varied to change their strength and hence focus.

Figure 1.3 Size relationships on a logarithmic scale of biological and chemical levels of organisation

Log scale (m)		Object	Methods of observation with their limit	Name of study or approach
10^2	100 m	Redwood tree		**Morphology** study of visible form – external structure
10^1	1 m	length of whale		
10^0				
10^{-1}			human eye	**Anatomy** study of the internal organisation of living things
10^{-2}				
10^{-3}	1 mm	cross section of giant nerve cell of squid — radius of giant marine algal cell	simple lens (hand-lens)	
10^{-4}		radius of giant amoeba — 40 μm range of diameter of most eukaryotic cells	classroom microscope (high power)	**Histology** study of tissues **Cytology** study of cells
10^{-5}			research quality light micro scope	
10^{-6}	1 μm	prokaryotic cells — 2 μm	electron micro- scope	**Ultra – structure** study of organelles and membranes
10^{-7}		smallest bacterium		
10^{-8}				
10^{-9}	1 nm	smallest virus — smaller macromolecules	no method of observation	**Molecular structure** and
10^{-10}	1 Å	small amino acid		**Atomic structure** by **chemical analysis**
10^{-11}		hydrogen atom		

Bacteria

Bacteria are very small and difficult to see, yet they occur in vast numbers. The total mass of living bacteria is estimated to be at least twenty times that of all animal life. Bacteria are simple in structure, and the fossil record indicates that some of the earliest cells were of this relatively simple construction. Bacteria are present in air, soil and water, they contaminate every surface and niche in our homes and on our bodies, and some even occur within parts of our bodies. Bacteria are often associated with disease, yet the bulk of bacteria are far from harmful. They are biochemically very active and fast growing, and their presence, together with that of fungi and green plants, is essential for the maintenance of life on Earth.

Figure 2.1 Rod-shaped bacteria (*Bacillus* sp.) observed by scanning electron microscopy (x 10 500)

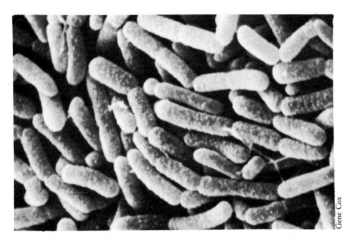

Size, shape and structure

Bacteria are unicellular but often occur clumped together, and in some species the individual cells actually remain joined to form simple filaments. The cells have a variety of sizes and shapes but they are all very small. In any population some cells will have divided recently whilst others will have reached their maximum and be about to divide, and thus there is always a range of sizes present. Because of their small size, the characteristic of shape is the most visible and important in the identification of bacteria. Three distinct forms are recognised, namely spheres, rods and spirals (or curved rods).

Figure 2.2. Range of cell size in bacteria

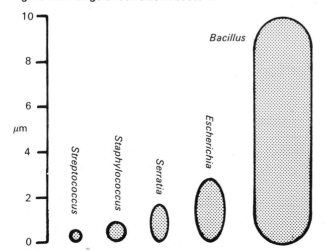

Most **human cells** are in the range 5–20 μm
Most **flowering plant cells** are in the range 10–50 μm

Figure 2.3 The three categories of bacterial shape

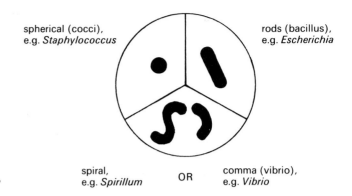

spherical (cocci), e.g. *Staphylococcus*

rods (bacillus), e.g. *Escherichia*

spiral, e.g. *Spirillum*   OR   comma (vibrio), e.g. *Vibrio*

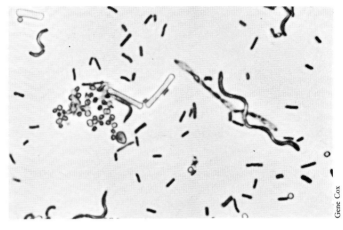

Figure 2.4 Cocci bacteria can be divided into the following generic groups, depending upon the way cells divide and how they subsequently adhere to each other

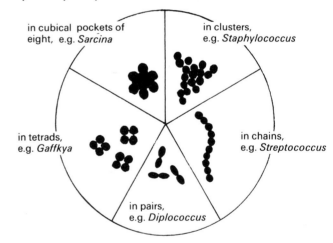

in cubical pockets of eight, e.g. *Sarcina*

in clusters, e.g. *Staphylococcus*

in tetrads, e.g. *Gaffkya*

in chains, e.g. *Streptococcus*

in pairs, e.g. *Diplococcus*

Figure 2.5 *Staphylococcus aureus* observed by scanning electron microscopy. Cells are seen in clusters like bunches of grapes (x 15 600)

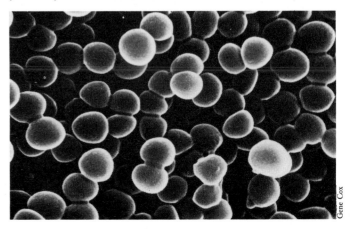

Figure 2.6 Structure of a bacterium based on electron micrographs

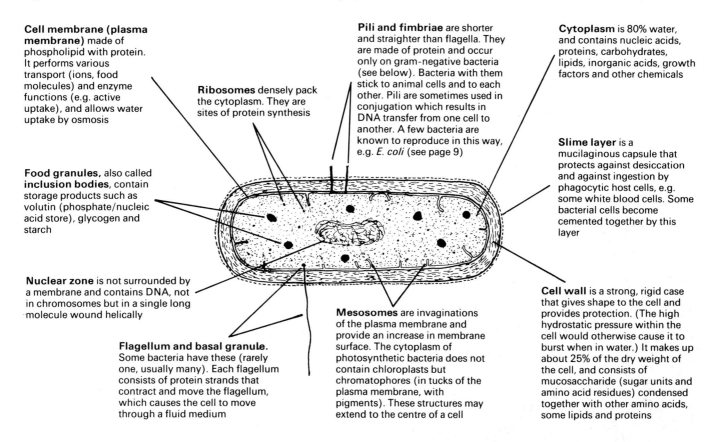

Cell membrane (plasma membrane) made of phospholipid with protein. It performs various transport (ions, food molecules) and enzyme functions (e.g. active uptake), and allows water uptake by osmosis

Ribosomes densely pack the cytoplasm. They are sites of protein synthesis

Pili and fimbriae are shorter and straighter than flagella. They are made of protein and occur only on gram-negative bacteria (see below). Bacteria with them stick to animal cells and to each other. Pili are sometimes used in conjugation which results in DNA transfer from one cell to another. A few bacteria are known to reproduce in this way, e.g. *E. coli* (see page 9)

Cytoplasm is 80% water, and contains nucleic acids, proteins, carbohydrates, lipids, inorganic acids, growth factors and other chemicals

Food granules, also called **inclusion bodies**, contain storage products such as volutin (phosphate/nucleic acid store), glycogen and starch

Slime layer is a mucilaginous capsule that protects against desiccation and against ingestion by phagocytic host cells, e.g. some white blood cells. Some bacterial cells become cemented together by this layer

Nuclear zone is not surrounded by a membrane and contains DNA, not in chromosomes but in a single long molecule wound helically

Mesosomes are invaginations of the plasma membrane and provide an increase in membrane surface. The cytoplasm of photosynthetic bacteria does not contain chloroplasts but chromatophores (in tucks of the plasma membrane, with pigments). These structures may extend to the centre of a cell

Flagellum and basal granule. Some bacteria have these (rarely one, usually many). Each flagellum consists of protein strands that contract and move the flagellum, which causes the cell to move through a fluid medium

Cell wall is a strong, rigid case that gives shape to the cell and provides protection. (The high hydrostatic pressure within the cell would otherwise cause it to burst when in water.) It makes up about 25% of the dry weight of the cell, and consists of mucosaccharide (sugar units and amino acid residues) condensed together with other amino acids, some lipids and proteins

The gram stain technique

Usually bacteria have to be stained to be identified, using an air-dried smear on a slide. A staining technique, first used by Christian Gram in 1884, distinguishes two types of bacteria: **gram-positive** and **gram-negative**.

Stage 1	Stage 2	Stage 3	Stage 4	Stage 5
Bacteria in the air-dried smear appear colourless	The smear is treated with crystal violet (a basic stain). All cells appear violet when the stain is washed from the slide	The smear is flooded with Lugol's iodine (a mordant treatment to combine the dye to those bacteria with which it will react)	The smear is now treated with a decolourising solution of acetone and alcohol. This removes the violet dye from those cells with which it has not reacted. **Gram-positive bacteria remain purple**	Finally the red dye safranin is briefly added as a counter stain. It is taken up by the colourless bacteria of the treated smear. **Gram-negative bacteria now appear red**. Gram-positive bacteria remain purple

The staining properties of gram-positive and gram-negative bacteria are due to differences in the chemical composition of the walls. **Gram-positive bacteria** have hardly any lipid in the wall. They are bacteria that may produce endospores (see page 9). Examples are *Staphylococci*, *Streptococci* and many others.

Gram-negative bacteria have chemically complex walls. There is less mucopeptide, more lipid (up to 20%) and protein. They are not affected by the naturally occurring enzyme *lysozyme* (e.g. in human tears). Lysozyme causes lysis: dissolving of the walls of many gram-positive bacteria so that they swell by osmosis and burst. Gram-negative bacteria may have flagella inserted at the end(s) of the cell (called polar flagella). Examples include *Salmonella* spp and many others.

Figure 2.7 Gram-positive rod bacteria and gram-negative cocci bacteria

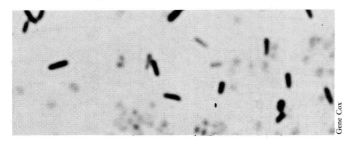
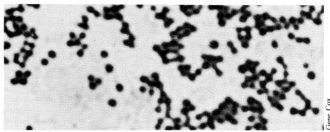

Growth of a bacterial colony

Bacteria grow and multiply extremely rapidly. In ideal conditions cell division may be as frequent as once every 20 minutes which, in theory, would enable a single cell to give rise to 100 000 000 cells in 15 hours. This volume of cells would occupy a large colony spot on the surface of a nutrient agar plate on which bacteria are often grown. This rate cannot be maintained indefinitely, but bacteria do occur in huge numbers. For example:

1 g of garden soil may contain　10 000 000 000 bacteria
1 cm³ fresh milk may contain　　　　　10 000 bacteria
1 cm³ sour milk may contain　33 000 000 000 bacteria

Because of the very large numbers of bacteria, populations have to be estimated from known dilutions from a measured sample in a method called the dilution plate technique (see facing page: 'Outline of Techniques').

Figure 2.9(i) Transmission electron micrograph of a section of a *Staphylococcus aureus* cell, showing its prokaryotic structure

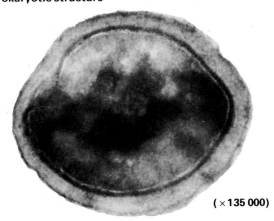

(× 135 000)

(ii) Early stage in cell division

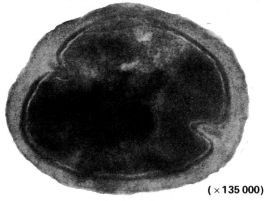

(× 135 000)

(iii) Cell division completed

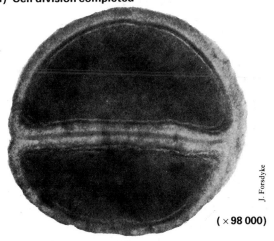

(× 98 000)

J. Forsdyke

Figure 2.8 Reproduction in bacteria: their cell cycle. A diagrammatic representation of the process of asexual reproduction by cell division in the bacterium *Esherichia coli*, taking approximately 45 minutes

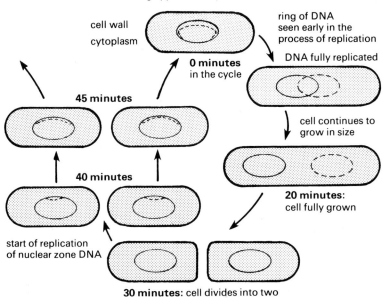

cell wall
cytoplasm

ring of DNA seen early in the process of replication

0 minutes in the cycle

DNA fully replicated

45 minutes

cell continues to grow in size

40 minutes

20 minutes: cell fully grown

start of replication of nuclear zone DNA

30 minutes: cell divides into two

Bacterial growth is dependent upon adequate water and an appropriate food supply. In addition, the following external factors are important.

pH	Temperature	Air with oxygen
Most bacteria are favoured by slightly alkaline conditions (pH 7.4). A few tolerate extremes of acidity or alkalinity	The range 25 to 45°C is favourable for the majority of bacteria. The extremes of survival are −5 to 80°C or higher	Most bacteria flourish in air (aerobes), but many can survive in the absence of oxygen (facultative anaerobes). Some flourish in anaerobic conditions (obligate anaerobes)

When a new medium is colonised there may be a lag phase (i.e. little or no reproduction) whilst the bacteria adjust to the new medium. During this time new enzymes are synthesised; it is a period of intense metabolic activity. There follows an exponential or logarithmic (log phase) of growth when the most spectacular growth-rate occurs. With time, the food store may be used up, excretory products accumulate, and the growth rate declines. Eventually, autolysis occurs leading to death of the colony.

Figure 2.10 Growth of a bacterial colony with time, following inoculation of a fresh medium

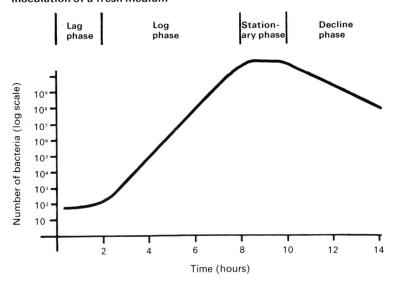

Lag phase　　Log phase　　Stationary phase　　Decline phase

Number of bacteria (log scale)

10^9
10^8
10^7
10^6
10^5
10^4
10^3
10^2
10

2　　4　　6　　8　　10　　12　　14

Time (hours)

Endospores

Some bacteria produce very resistant spores during unfavourable conditions. The spores have great resistance to cold, heat, pH change, desiccation and the effects of chemicals. Only certain gram-positive bacteria produce endospores (see page 7 and the photograph on page 14, figure 2.16).

The endospore in the life-cycle of a bacterium

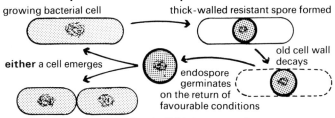

growing bacterial cell — thick-walled resistant spore formed

either a cell emerges — old cell wall decays — endospore germinates on the return of favourable conditions

or the spore contents immediately divide into two cells

Feeding

Bacteria require an energy source and a source of raw materials (nutrients). **Energy** may come from the metabolism of sugars or fats, from light, or from chemical reactions. The **raw materials** needed for growth and reproduction include **carbon**, which may come from sources as diverse as jet fuel, engine oil, wood, sugar or gaseous CO_2 (substances which can be utilised by bacteria are termed biodegradable). Other requirements are **nitrogen**, possibly from N_2 gas, ammonium salts, amino acids or proteins; **inorganic salts**, usually PO_4^{3-}, SO_4^{2-}, Mg^{2+}, K^+, Ca^{2+}, and Fe^{3+} ions; **water**; and occasionally metabolites such as vitamins. These nutrients may be obtained in two different ways.

Sexual reproduction

Certain bacteria reproduce by conjugation.

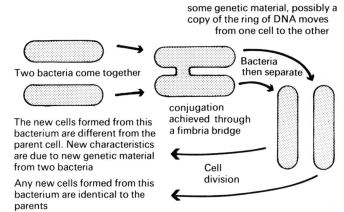

some genetic material, possibly a copy of the ring of DNA moves from one cell to the other

Two bacteria come together

Bacteria then separate

conjugation achieved through a fimbria bridge

Cell division

The new cells formed from this bacterium are different from the parent cell. New characteristics are due to new genetic material from two bacteria

Any new cells formed from this bacterium are identical to the parents

Autotrophic bacteria use light energy or the energy from chemical reactions to combine carbon (usually from CO_2) and hydrogen (usually from water) to produce sugar. With this sugar and certain ions they manufacture all other requirements. Photosynthetic autotrophs include the green sulphur bacteria and the purple sulphur bacteria. Chemosynthetic autotrophs include *Nitrosomonas* and *Nitrobacter* (see page 10) and *Thiobacillus ferro-oxydans* (see page 12).

Heterotrophic bacteria consume dead or living organisms or other organic matter such as rubbish or fuels etc. as a source of energy and nutrients. These bacteria secrete digestive enzymes into their food; digestion occurs outside the cell wall and the products are selectively absorbed into the cell.

Culturing bacteria

Bacteria are cultured (grown) on, or in, media that are designed to supply the cells with all their nutritional requirements (that is a complete culture medium). Aseptic techniques, in which apparatus and equipment are kept free of stray micro-organisms, are used to prevent contamination of bacterial cultures and of the surrounding environment. Although most bacteria are harmless, bacteriologists treat all bacterial cultures as potentially dangerous. A few are extremely dangerous.

OUTLINE OF TECHNIQUES – an introduction to the process and the terminology of culturing bacteria: NOT a practical guide

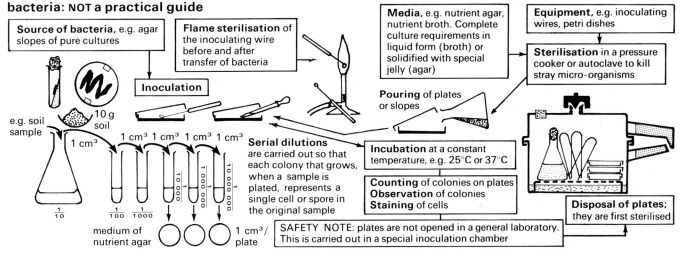

Source of bacteria, e.g. agar slopes of pure cultures

Flame sterilisation of the inoculating wire before and after transfer of bacteria

Inoculation

Media, e.g. nutrient agar, nutrient broth. Complete culture requirements in liquid form (broth) or solidified with special jelly (agar)

Pouring of plates or slopes

Equipment, e.g. inoculating wires, petri dishes

Sterilisation in a pressure cooker or autoclave to kill stray micro-organisms

e.g. soil sample

10 g soil

1 cm³

1 cm³ 1 cm³ 1 cm³ 1 cm³

Serial dilutions are carried out so that each colony that grows, when a sample is plated, represents a single cell or spore in the original sample

$\frac{1}{10}$ $\frac{1}{100}$ $\frac{1}{1000}$

medium of nutrient agar

1 cm³/ plate

Incubation at a constant temperature, e.g. 25°C or 37°C

Counting of colonies on plates
Observation of colonies
Staining of cells

SAFETY NOTE: plates are not opened in a general laboratory. This is carried out in a special inoculation chamber

Disposal of plates; they are first sterilised

Why some bacteria are dangerous

The human body is continuously exposed to contamination by micro-organisms, but very few harmful organisms are able to establish themselves. This is due mainly to:

(a) the inhibitory effects of our natural secretions,

(b) the invading bacteria having to compete with harmless micro-organism populations already resident in the body.

Thus we are usually infected with micro-organisms, but only rarely are we diseased.

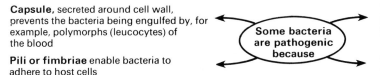

Capsule, secreted around cell wall, prevents the bacteria being engulfed by, for example, polymorphs (leucocytes) of the blood

Pili or fimbriae enable bacteria to adhere to host cells

Some bacteria are pathogenic because

Exotoxins and enzymes that overcome host-cell defences. Secreted by the bacteria they kill or injure the cell. These secretions are all proteins

Endotoxins are proteins, lipids or polysaccharides from the bacterial cell wall, liberated only on the decay of the bacterial cell. They cause fever and shock

Examples of exotoxins

Clostridium botulinum on decaying food in the absence of air produces one of the most potent poisons known to man. *Staphylococcus aureus* produces heat-stable toxins that attack the gut and cause 'food poisoning'.

Examples of endotoxins

The large molecules of lipopolysaccharide (lipid and carbohydrate combined together) that are a part of the outer wall of gram-negative organisms such as *Salmonella typhi*, which causes the fever and shock of typhoid fever.

Examples of useful bacteria

1. Bacteria in the cycling of nutrients

Plants and animals use elements and nutrients that occur at or near the earth's surface, and supplies of these nutrients are limited. For survival of life the materials in one organism must eventually be made available to other organisms. Elements such as carbon, nitrogen, sulphur, phosphorus and iron (along with many other substances found in minute amounts) are cycled, and these cycles are 'driven' directly or indirectly by energy from the sun. These processes are summarised in the Ecological Triangle, figure 2.11. The breakdown by saprophytes of green plants, their products and their predators (herbivores and carnivores) makes the nutrients and elements available for re-use. These saprophytes include many fungi (see page 45) and many bacteria, and the process is illustrated by the nitrogen cycle and carbon cycle.

Figure 2.11 Ecological triangle showing the pyramid of biomass and both the cycling of materials and the energy flow within it

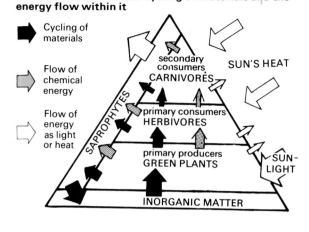

The nitrogen cycle

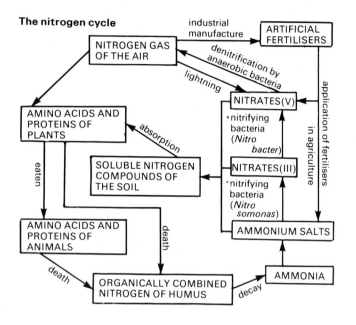

* Nitrifying bacteria are chemosynthetic autotrophs, using energy from exothermic chemical reactions,

by *Nitrosomonas* spp

e.g. $2NH_3 + 3O_2 \xrightarrow[\text{by } Nitrosomonas \text{ spp}]{} 2HNO_2 + 2H_2O + energy$

e.g. $2HNO_3 + O_2 \xrightarrow[\text{by } Nitrobacter \text{ spp}]{} 2HNO_3 + energy$

The carbon cycle

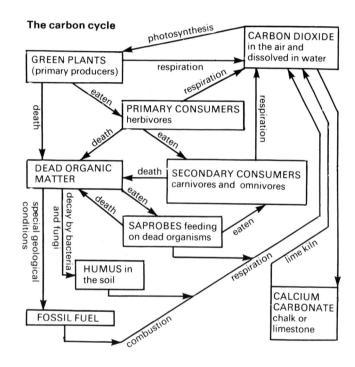

The formation and functioning of leguminous root nodules

Bacteria of the genus *Rhizobium* occur in nearly all types of soil. Many leguminous plants (family Leguminosae, e.g. clover, peas, beans) become hosts to species of *Rhizobium* during the growing season, forming root nodules which contain these bacteria within the host cells.

Figure 2.12 Root nodules on the roots of a broad bean

Root nodules form on the lateral roots after *Rhizobium* bacteria have entered from the soil. Here nodules are seen at the end of the growing season, on part of the root system.

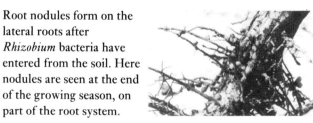

Tip of root of a leguminous plant root in section, with central vascular tissue

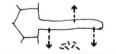

Root hair releases a chemical into the soil. This is detected by *Rhizobium* bacteria

region of root hairs

region of elongation

growing point
root cap

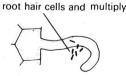

bacteria pass into the root hair cells and multiply

Bacteria produce hormone-like chemical which causes root hairs to curve

Large cells of the root cortex become filled with *Rhizobium*

path taken by bacteria as they invade and penetrate the root

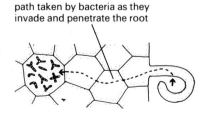

The *Rhizobium* become large, irregular-shaped bacterial cells. They produce and release plant growth hormone. This helps induce the formation of a mass of cells—the nodule

Tap root system with numerous root nodules

2. The bacteriology of milk and its products

Milk is liquid food produced by female mammals for their young. It provides a balanced diet, low only in vitamin C and iron. As formed in the cow's udder, it is biologically sterile (in a healthy animal).

As it leaves the mammary gland via the teat, the milk quickly acquires a characteristic flora of non-pathogenic bacteria. If these bacteria are not checked by low temperatures and pasteurisation they quickly cause the milk to go sour. Milk passing into dairy equipment is raw and untreated. It may acquire further bacterial contamination if the equipment is unclean.

Untreated milk may contain harmful bacteria, e.g. the brucellosis causing bacteria *Brucella abortus*, causing contagious abortion in cattle and undulent fever in humans.

TREATED MILK

Pasteurisation	Sterilisation	Ultra high temperature (UHT)
Milk is heated to 72°C for 20 seconds and then quickly cooled to below 10°C. This destroys the majority of the bacteria without harming milk quality.	Milk is filtered, violently mixed to disperse the cream into tiny droplets (homogenised), bottled and then heated to over 100°C for about 25 minutes. There is a loss of flavour and some colour change.	Milk is heated to 132°C for one second and then placed in a sterile container under aseptic conditions. This kills all bacteria and spores. There is little loss of flavour.

Figure 2.13 *Lactobacillus bulgaricus*, **a bacterium used as a 'starter' in the production of yoghurt from pasteurised milk** (× 4 375)

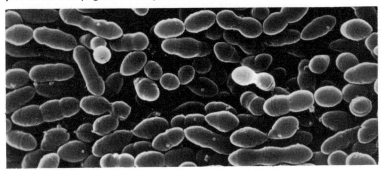

Cross-section of root with nodule

Nitrogen from the air is reduced to ammonia by *Rhizobium*, using the enzyme nitrogenase (see page 18). Ammonia is combined with organic acid to make amino acids. The nodules are pink/red due to haemoglobin that is formed in the nodule by the host (leguminous) cells. Nitrogenase enzyme is inhibited (poisoned) by oxygen. The haemoglobin may regulate or control the oxygen concentration, and facilitate nitrogen fixation

At the end of the growing season the nodules break down, releasing bacteria and ammonium compounds into the soil. In this way leguminous plants increase the fertility of the soil for all plants.

Pasteurised milk is drunk as it is or used in the manufacture of yoghurt, cheese, butter, or milk powder.

(a) Yoghurt. This is a culture of two different bacteria which is added to milk at 40–45°C to ferment lactose to lactic acid and to curdle and sour the milk. One of the bacteria used is shown in figure 2.13.

(b) Cheese. To pasteurised milk are added:
    (i) rennet, a preparation of calf stomach, containing renin to coagulate casein (milk protein),
    (ii) 'starting culture' (inoculum) of *Streptococcus lactis*, to ferment lactose to lactic acid. The pH drops from 7 to 4.5.
This causes the milk to separate into CURD and WHEY.

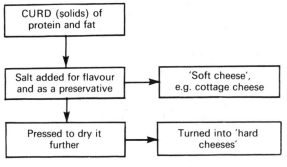

Further bacterial and fungal action is required to introduce the characteristic flavour and aroma of particular cheeses.

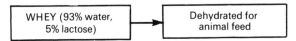

(c) Butter. Cream is separated from the milk, churned to change the fat globules into granules, and the solid fraction is treated with starting cultures of *Streptococcus lactis* and *Leuconostoc lactis* to sour the lactose and produce flavour and aroma by bacterial enzyme action.

(d) Dried milk powder. This is used for cooking or to make feed for babies. It is a versatile product with keeping quality but little flavour.

Powdered milk for babies is useful where breast milk is not available. The problems with bottle feeding arise from:
    (i) bacterial contamination; careful sterilisation of equipment is essential,
    (ii) malnutrition; the powder must be made up into milk of the correct strength.
The misuse of powdered milk has reached tragic proportions in some Third World countries where people have been persuaded by advertisements to change to this method of baby feeding unnecessarily.

3. Bacteria and genetic engineering

The nuclear material in the bacterial cell is a single strand of DNA in the form of a ring or helix. Prior to cell division this strand of DNA (it is of the same chemical composition as in eukaryotes) replicates, and one copy passes into each daughter cell. (This is shown in figure 2.8, page 8.) The unusual feature of bacterial DNA is that it can be changed by addition of short lengths of DNA from the cell of a closely related bacterium. The process may be brought about by an invading bacterial virus (called a phage, see page 15).

DNA controls and directs the biochemical activity of the cells by directing protein and enzyme synthesis. In this way DNA controls growth, development and the functioning of the whole organism. Because bacterial DNA does not occur in pairs as it does in eukaryotic chromosomes (the eukaryotes have two alleles to every gene) it means that any changes that are brought about in the bacterial DNA may result in more or less immediate changes in the functioning of the bacterial cell. These naturally occurring changes or accidents of DNA addition have been much studied, and techniques for engineering such changes in bacteria, using unrelated DNA from viruses, other bacteria, and from eukaryotic cells have been developed (called genetic engineering or recombinant genetics). Bacterial strains have been made which permit relatively inexpensive synthesis of vitamins, hormones (e.g. human insulin for diabetics), antibiotics and drugs such as human interferon, an anti-viral agent.

The danger associated with genetic engineering, is that, inadvertently, some very harmful gene may be added to the DNA of a ubiquitous and normally harmless bacterium of the human micro-flora, which might then escape into the population and multiply. Stringent safeguards have been laid down to prevent such an event, e.g. genetic engineering being limited to species that only prosper under abnormal physiological conditions, not occurring in the human body.

4. Vaccines

Robert Koch (1843–1910) isolated *Bacillus anthracis* from anthrax sufferers and established the rules (now known as Koch's postulates) by which it is judged when an organism is a pathogen and not just a casual member of the normal body flora.

Koch's postulates
(a) The same organism must be found in all cases of the disease.

(b) The organism must be isolated and grown in pure culture from the infected host.

(c) The organism from the pure culture must reproduce the disease when inoculated into a susceptible host.

(d) The organism must be isolated in pure culture from the experimentally infected animal.

Figure 2.14 *Bacillus anthracis*, a large, broad-celled gram-positive bacterium that requires aerobic conditions. The rods have almost square corners and cytoplasm that stains irregularly (× 2000)

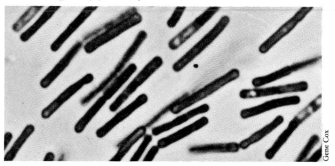

It was also with *B. anthracis* that the first systematic vaccinations were conducted.

A vaccine is a suspension of killed, or living but inactivated organisms which, when inoculated into the body, act as an antigen causing development of antibodies that render the body immune or, at least, resistant to infection by that organism. Humans can be infected with the anthrax bacillus by contact with hides of infected animals. Anthrax is primarily a disease of sheep, cattle and other herbivorous animals. An infection occurs in the skin, but the bacterium invades the blood and produces a toxin which acts on the central nervous system causing breathing to cease. Louis Pasteur (1822–95), working with farm animals, kept some anthrax bacilli at 42°C (i.e. at above body temperature) and produced a less virulent (attenuated) strain. This, when injected into the body, was no longer capable of causing anthrax, but it did induce immunity to the disease. When the virulent strain was injected subsequently, the animals did not contract anthrax.

From earlier times people were aware that some individuals have, or acquire, immunity to certain diseases. Edward Jenner (1749–1823) observed that many patients who were in contact with cattle had apparently acquired immunity to the usually fatal disease smallpox. He believed that this immunity was acquired following an attack of the similar but much milder disease cowpox; the cowpox being transmitted to people from the cows they worked with. It was Jenner who first used the technique of inoculation. He gave people cowpox and then showed that they subsequently acquired immunity to smallpox.

5. Microbial mining

It is now necessary to use lower and lower grade ore as the explosion in demand for metals for industrial and manufacturing uses has already outstripped the supply of accessible, high-grade deposits of appropriate ores. The deliberate use of bacteria to assist in recovery of metals from low-grade ores is a quite recent development. In the bacterial leaching of copper for example, the metal is being economically recovered from old mine waste containing only 0.25–0.50% copper.

The tiny, rod-shaped *Thiobacillus ferro-oxidans* occurs naturally in ore dumps in the absence of light and in an acid medium. The bacterium 'eats rock', i.e. it is chemolithotrophic. It oxidises sulphides to sulphates and iron(II) to iron(III) ions.

chalcopyrite $CuFeS_2 + 2Fe_2(SO_4)_3 + 2H_2O + 3O_2 \rightarrow CuSO_4 + 5FeSO_4 + 2H_2SO_4 + ENERGY$

The energy released in the reaction is used in part to fix carbon dioxide and water to make sugar, with oxygen as a waste produce (autotrophic nutrition). The remainder of the energy is lost as heat and warms the ore dump, further speeding the bacterial extraction of copper. The bacterium thrives best in the temperature range 20–35°C.

The process of copper extraction

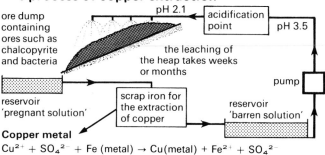

Copper metal

$Cu^{2+} + SO_4^{2-} + Fe (metal) \rightarrow Cu(metal) + Fe^{2+} + SO_4^{2-}$

The bacterium consumes the ore by transferring electrons from iron ions and sulphide ions making the ore more soluble. The electrons are transferred to oxygen to produce water and give up energy which is coupled to ATP synthesis.

Bacteria in water and sewage

Sewage is a mixture of organic matter in water, rich in bacteria which aerobically digest sewage. This process needs to be contained and completed at a sewage plant because if raw sewage is discharged into rivers the bacterial consumption of dissolved oxygen is so great that other organisms are deprived of oxygen and die of asphyxia. Oxygen gas is only slightly soluble in water and it is shortage of oxygen due to excessive bacterial activity rather than the presence of a poison in sewage that kills larger animals in sewage polluted rivers and streams. This feature of water quality is known as its Biological Oxygen Demand (BOD). It is defined as the amount of oxygen absorbed biologically by one litre of the water sample in five days at 20°C.

Treatment of sewage

Bacteria, with other micro-organisms, turn sewage into re-usable and inoffensive substances.

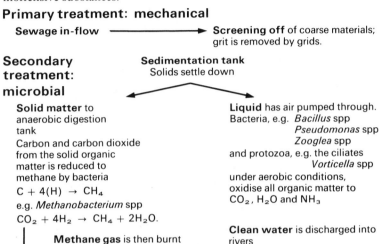

Primary treatment: mechanical

Sewage in-flow ⟶ **Screening off** of coarse materials; grit is removed by grids.

Secondary treatment: microbial

Sedimentation tank Solids settle down

Solid matter to anaerobic digestion tank
Carbon and carbon dioxide from the solid organic matter is reduced to methane by bacteria
$C + 4(H) \rightarrow CH_4$
e.g. *Methanobacterium* spp
$CO_2 + 4H_2 \rightarrow CH_4 + 2H_2O$.

Methane gas is then burnt to power the sewage plant

Liquid has air pumped through. Bacteria, e.g. *Bacillus* spp
Pseudomonas spp
Zooglea spp
and protozoa, e.g. the ciliates
Vorticella spp
under aerobic conditions, oxidise all organic matter to CO_2, H_2O and NH_3

Clean water is discharged into rivers

Remaining solid matter is flash-dried over a gas flame to dry and sterilise: it is then sold as **fertiliser**

Control of water-borne disease

1. In Third World countries

A very deep well surrounded by a concrete lip to exclude surface contamination is the safest source of drinking water.

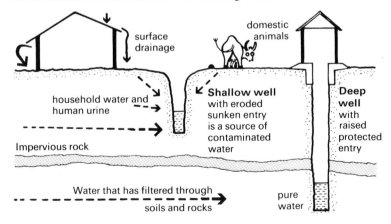

surface drainage

domestic animals

household water and human urine

Shallow well with eroded sunken entry is a source of contaminated water

Deep well with raised protected entry

Impervious rock

Water that has filtered through soils and rocks

pure water

Contamination of drinking water by sewage

The human small and large intestines house a huge and characteristic microflora. They are mostly commensal bacteria, but a few bacteria live mutualistically, providing their host with vitamins, e.g. vitamin K and vitamin B complex.
Escherichia coli is an extremely common component of the human intestines, and it is responsible for faecal odour. (Human faeces are 50% bacteria.) Water purity tests check for the presence of this bacterium as evidence of contamination of the drinking water supply by sewage.

Figure 2.15 *Escherichia coli,* **a bacillus that is part of the normal flora of the human intestinal tract (×16 600).** Rods show fimbriae (pili), filamentous appendages which are shorter and smaller than flagella. They cause bacteria to adhere, and they may also be involved in the sexual transfer of genetic material in conjugation (see page 9)

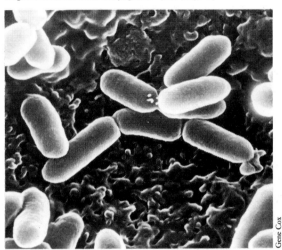

Gene Cox

2. In Developed countries

In situations where urban conurbations are crowded together, the water supply to one city (e.g. London) is the river that drains sewage works of towns up-stream (e.g. Reading). The steps in purification are:

Untreated water

AERATION	oxidation of organic matter by micro-organisms
COAGULATION	aluminium sulphate is added, causing particles to clump together
SEDIMENTATION	coagulated material settles out
FILTRATION	using sand
CHLORINATION	at quite low concentration destroys all living things

Tap water

Water-borne diseases of consequence include:

Cholera

Cholera is caused by *Vibrio cholerae*. This is very common amongst the people in Bangladesh and the Far East; it is said to be endemic there. It is spread by people where the sewage is not correctly disposed of and contaminates the water supply. The patient vomits and has severe diarrhoea. Death can be quick due to dehydration and shock. The bacterium produces a powerful toxin that inflames the lining of the intestines.

Typhoid

Typhoid is caused by *Salmonella typhi*. This is typically a disease of overcrowded communities, where the people have become weakened by the effects of poverty and starvation. It causes high fever, slow pulse-rate, irritation of the intestine and diarrhoea. Healthy carriers occur and can pass the infection by handling food for other people.

Some bacterial diseases of Man

1. Botulism

Botulism is a poisoning due to a nerve toxin called botulin, produced by the rod-shaped bacterium *Clostridium botulinum* under anaerobic conditions. The bacterium occurs in soil, but the danger to man arises if, in the canning of food, the temperature is not raised high enough to destroy any endospores which may have got in. Today cases of the disease are very rare. Botulin is one of the most poisonous toxins known, but it is not produced in food if the food is:

(a) in the presence of air,
(b) very acid, that is below pH 5,
(c) preserved in 8% or greater sodium chloride solution,
(d) preserved in 50% or greater sugar solution.

Furthermore, proper cooking inactivates any of the botulin that is present, although botulin can occur in incorrectly canned foods, such as asparagus, corn, peas, pepper, spinach, ham or sausage.

2. Diphtheria

This disease is caused by the bacterium *Corynebacterium diphtheriae*. It is spread by droplet infection (e.g. sneezing) from infected to healthy people, and produces a local infection of the nose, throat and larynx. The bacterium releases a powerful toxin that can kill by damage to the heart. In developed countries this disease has been virtually eradicated by vaccination. The vaccine is prepared by extracting the toxin from a culture of the bacteria and rendering it harmless with formalin. When the vaccine is injected into a human (diphtheria is purely a human disease) it causes antibody production and hence immunity.

3. Tetanus

The tetanus-causing bacterium *Clostridium tetani* is an obligate anaerobic bacillus that exists in soil and in the gut of man. The bacterium is sensitive to penicillin, but it produces extremely resistant endospores. Deep body wounds may be deprived of oxygen owing to damaged blood supply and to the metabolism of the contaminating bacteria. Such wounds may be contaminated with *C. tetani*. Under anaerobic conditions the bacterium grows and releases a powerful toxin into the bloodstream. This is transported around the body and interferes with impulse conduction at the synapses of nerves causing convulsive contraction of voluntary muscles. Tetanus is most prevalent among those wounded in war, and in children, particularly infants in rural Asia, where the baby's umbilical cord stump may be contaminated with soil or faeces. Tetanus prevention is easier than treatment. In developed countries children are treated with tetanus toxin which has been modified in a laboratory so that its poisonous properties are lost but its antigenic properties remain (called tetanus toxoid). Immunity acquired in this way is not permanently retained by the body, and booster doses to re-acquire immunity become necessary from time to time.

Figure 2.16 *Clostridium tetani,* **the agent of tetanus (lockjaw)** (× 4 200). These bacteria are obligate anaerobes; they cannot grow in the presence of oxygen. They are large, motile gram-positive rods that produce extremely resistant endospores. These spores occur as terminal swellings that make the whole structure resemble a miniature drumstick

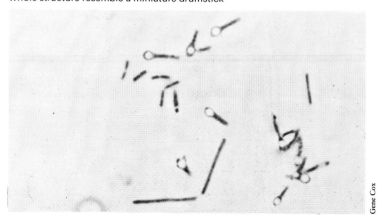

Gene Cox

4. Tuberculosis (TB)

Tuberculosis is caused by *Mycobacterium tuberculosis* which may be inhaled or swallowed. It attacks the lungs, and in elderly, ill or malnourished people, it leads to serious illness and death due to progressive destruction of the lung tissue.

It causes a major health problem world-wide since there are so many people who are malnourished and who live in cramped unsanitary homes on the edge of cities. In developed countries there is good control of TB. This may be attributed to:

(a) improvements in the general standard of living and nutrition,
(b) eradication of TB in cattle and the pasteurisation of milk,
(c) development of drugs for the control of the disease in those affected,
(d) early detection of infection by mass radiographic screening,
(e) the introduction of effective BCG (Bacillus-Calmette-Guérin) vaccination which involves inoculating 12 to 13-year-olds with an injection of living but inactivated (attenuated) cells. Before treatment of an individual with BCG, it is necessary to test whether they are already suffering from TB or have natural immunity. The reaction of the skin to the products of dead bacilli is tested; those whose skin reacts strongly (their skin swells and reddens at the test site) either have immunity or the disease.

5. Whooping cough (Pertussis)

Whooping cough is an acute infection of the respiratory tract. It leads to violent coughing and fever. It is caused by a small, gram-negative coccobacillus (broad oval bacteria – see pages 6 and 7) called *Bordetella pertussis*. It does not invade the bloodstream but toxins from the bacteria cause the fever, and as the organism grows, a thick ropey mucus is produced from the lungs. Whooping cough was once a common infectious disease of children causing very high mortality in infants under one year of age. It is hard to treat, but vaccination with an injection of killed bacteria, administered in the second or third month of life is totally effective in prevention. The vaccine, of dead bacilli, is administered together with diphtheria and tetanus toxoid. A total of three, monthly injections is given. Occasionally whooping cough vaccine causes allergic convulsions and very rarely may produce permanent brain damage. The number of cases of brain damage after vaccination is 1 in 50 000 vaccinations. The risks of contracting whooping cough are far greater than that of immunisation. However, children with another illness must not be vaccinated until they are well again. Children who suffer from convulsions should not be treated at all, and those who show symptoms of nervous system disorder during the vaccination sequence should have no further injections of the vaccine.

6. Venereal disease

Venereal diseases are infections which are spread from person to person during sexual intercourse or other sexual contact. Some babies may be infected in the womb or at birth by an infected mother. The most common venereal diseases are syphilis and gonorrhoea. These diseases can be cured with antibiotics, provided thorough treatment is given at an early stage.

7. Boils

Boils are due to *Staphylococcus aureus* (see figure 2.5, page 6). This bacterium forms golden yellow colonies when cultured. It occurs as part of the normal bacterial flora of the nose, but it causes infection when it gets into the skin at the base of a hair follicle, or through a cut.

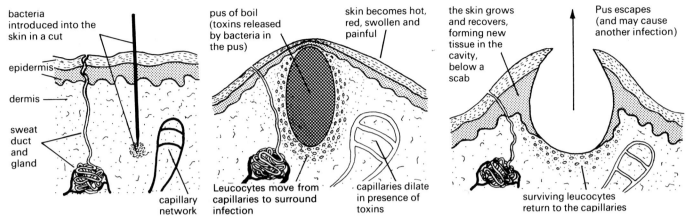

bacteria introduced into the skin in a cut

epidermis

dermis

sweat duct and gland

capillary network

pus of boil (toxins released by bacteria in the pus)

Leucocytes move from capillaries to surround infection

skin becomes hot, red, swollen and painful

capillaries dilate in presence of toxins

the skin grows and recovers, forming new tissue in the cavity, below a scab

Pus escapes (and may cause another infection)

surviving leucocytes return to the capillaries

Acne and the changes in the skin at puberty

Skin texture alters at puberty, particularly in the male, from being dry and smooth to greasy and sweaty. This is just one of the sex-hormone-stimulated upheavals in the body at this time, and under hormone assault the skin may show enhanced susceptibility to infection (acne). The problem recedes as the skin adapts and settles to the new concentration of sex hormones in the body.

Phage – a virus that is specific to a bacterial host

Viruses are agents of disease that are not alive outside the host cell. A virus consists of a coiled strand of nucleic acid (DNA or RNA) enclosed in a protein coat. They are capable of replication only within a host cell. Viruses are often specific to a particular species of host organism; a virus specific to a bacterium is called a phage. Viruses are too small to be observed by the light microscope; they are viewed with the electron microscope.

Viruses cause breakdown of the cells they attack and this appears as a lesion on larger hosts and as complete dissolution (lysis) of bacterial colonies which become watery and transparent. Phage particles appear to have a head and tail structure. The phage attaches itself (or becomes attached) by its tail structure to the host cell membrane and injects its core of DNA in the host cell. Viruses of higher plants and animals similarly have a coat (made of protein) and a core of DNA or RNA, but the whole cell enters the host cell before the nucleic acid separates. Without its coat or sheath the virus can no longer infect other cells. It is called a viron at this stage. Within the host cell the viron causes replication of viral nucleic acid and protein.

Figure 2.17 Electron micrograph of a stained preparation of the phage (virus) that parasitises the bacterium *Lactobacillus bulgaricus* (× 150 000)

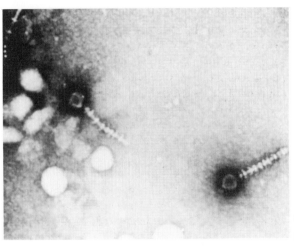

Gene Cox

The structure of the phage
(interpretation of the electron micrograph, above)

hexagonal head

made of protein

tail

coiled strand of DNA

cross bars and tail plate of uncertain function

Stages in the parasitisation of the host and replication of the phage

the virus becomes attached to the wall

1.

ring of DNA

bacterium wall

Virus DNA only enters the host bacterial cell

2.

The bacterial DNA breaks down. The virus DNA is replicated

3.

The virus coat is synthesised

4.

Virulent phage

OR

Temperate phage

At some later stage the temperate bacteriophage becomes virulent

Just occasionally temperate relationships are established in which the virus DNA attaches to the host DNA and both are replicated in step

bacterial cell dividing

bacterial DNA

virus DNA

Temperate bacteriophage has replicated and divided

Virus is assembled from DNA and coat

5.

Lysis occurs

Host cell bursts open releasing virus particles

6.

Blue-green algae

Blue-green algae grow where there is light and moisture. They often occur on shaded bare soil, as gelatinous encrustations on moist rocks or posts, on other terrestrial plants, in the plankton layer in freshwater or marine environments, attached to other organisms and as a matted blanket on pond mud. They are extremely small; the cell diameter is typically 2–3 μm and never exceeds 10 μm. Blue-green algae have been identified in fossil remains two billion (2×10^9) years old. Earliest life forms may have been very similar to present day blue-greens. Recent studies of these tiny plants using the electron microscope have shown them to be prokaryotic organisms, like bacteria, and not true algae. In colour they are often green or blue-green, but they may appear dark purple, brown or red under certain conditions.

Figure 3.1 *Anabaena* **sp. and diatoms on the surface of other pond organisms** (× 480)

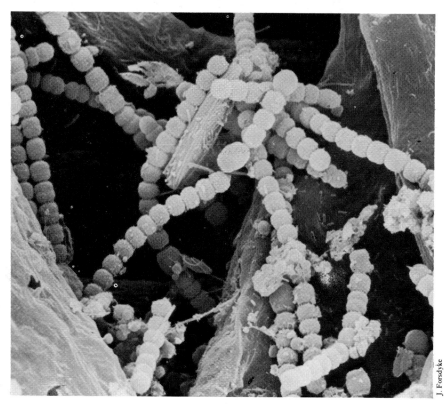

Cell structure

Cells may occur singly or as colonies of individuals held together by the cell sheath, apparently without co-ordination of activity. Each cell is surrounded by a wall of mucopeptides (polysaccharides with protein) and a slimy gelatinous sheath. The cytoplasm contains coiled DNA (but no true nucleus), photosynthetic lamellae and ribosomes. In addition to chlorophyll, the cell contains supplementary pigments, such as phycocyanin in blue-green forms, and phycoerythrin in red forms. The membranes in the cells are made of protein and lipid, and appear to originate by invagination of the cell plasma membrane (plasmalemma).

Figure 3.2 Transmission electron micrograph of a section of *Anabaena fossaguae* **with explanatory illustration** (× 30 000)

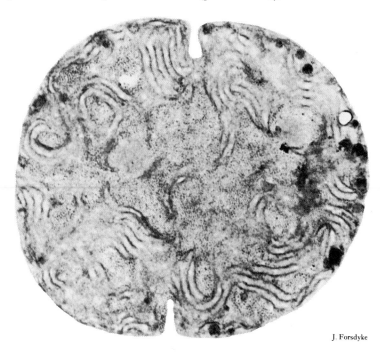

J. Forsdyke

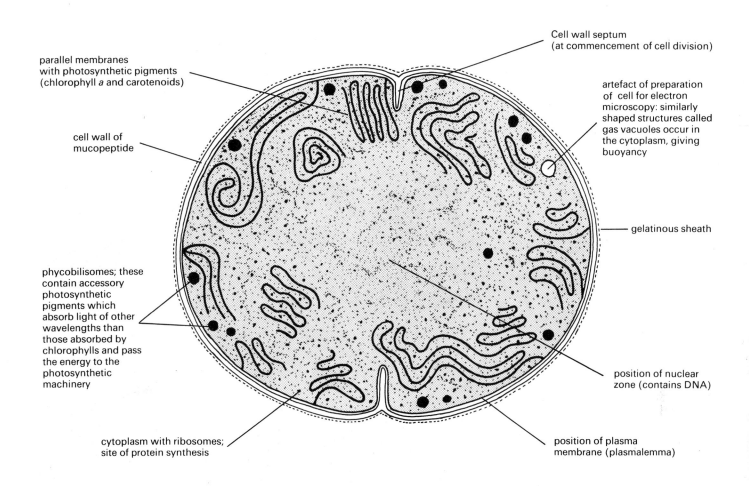

parallel membranes with photosynthetic pigments (chlorophyll *a* and carotenoids)

cell wall of mucopeptide

phycobilisomes; these contain accessory photosynthetic pigments which absorb light of other wavelengths than those absorbed by chlorophylls and pass the energy to the photosynthetic machinery

cytoplasm with ribosomes; site of protein synthesis

Cell wall septum (at commencement of cell division)

artefact of preparation of cell for electron microscopy: similarly shaped structures called gas vacuoles occur in the cytoplasm, giving buoyancy

gelatinous sheath

position of nuclear zone (contains DNA)

position of plasma membrane (plasmalemma)

Cell division

Cell division is preceded by replication and separation of the nucleic acid in the nuclear zone, as in bacteria (see figure 2.8, page 8).

Figure 3.3 *Anabaena* sp. cells immediately after division has been completed, shown stained, sectioned and viewed by transmission electron microscopy (× 37 600)

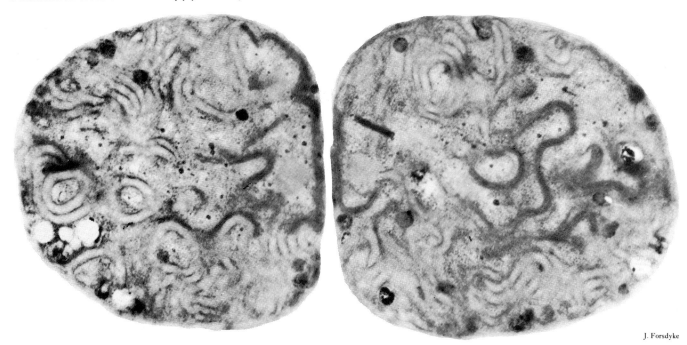

J. Forsdyke

Nitrogen fixation in blue-green algae

Relatively few organisms are capable of reducing atmospheric nitrogen to ammonia and combining this into organic acids to make amino acids and protein. Certain bacteria do this (see page 10) and so do blue-green algae.

Pathway of gaseous nitrogen fixation

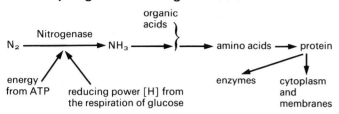

The enzyme nitrogenase is destroyed or inactivated by oxygen; cells able to fix nitrogen have to protect the enzyme from oxygen.

In *Anabaena* sp. nitrogen fixation is restricted to thick-walled cells called heterocysts which do not have photosynthetic pigments. The plant filament contains many photosynthetic cells which produce sugar (and oxygen as a waste product) and a few heterocyst cells that generate combined nitrogen. This represents simple division of labour within the filament. When the external medium is rich in organic nitrogen the heterocysts disappear from the filament.

Figure 3.4(i) Scanning electron micrograph of part of an *Anabaena* sp. filament with heterocyst ($\times$ 920)

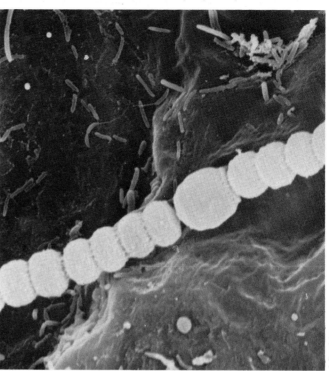

J. Forsdyke

Figure 3.4(ii) Annotated drawing, showing the structure and function of a heterocyst cell

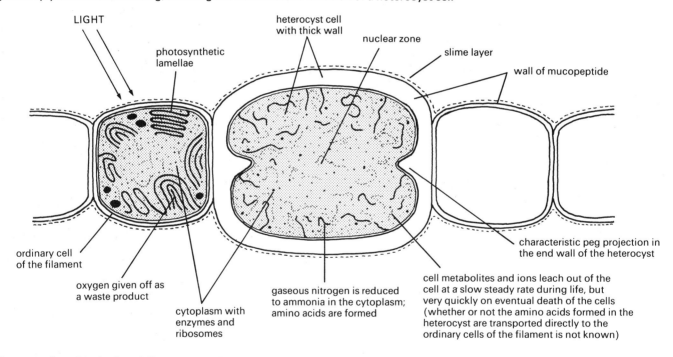

The ecological significance of blue-green algae

The appearance of blue-green algae on the Earth must have been a major ecological point of no return for at least three reasons.

1. Blue-green algae were almost certainly the first photosynthetic organisms. In their metabolism, water is split into hydrogen (reducing power) and the waste product oxygen escapes from the cells into the atmosphere. Thus, oxygen started to accumulate in the atmosphere and currently the concentration has reached almost 21%. The presence of oxygen gas permits a much more economical utilisation of foods. (All forms of anaerobic respiration are wasteful of resources.)

After the appearance of blue-green algae, aerobic respiration evolved and from this followed the possibility of larger more efficient heterotrophs (herbivores, carnivores and omnivores).

2. Following the accumulation of gaseous oxygen (O_2), ozone (O_3) started to form, and began to collect in the upper atmosphere. Ozone absorbs ultraviolet (UV) radiation which comes from the Sun. It is likely that UV radiation was one of the original energy sources that might have initiated biochemical change and generated life from non-living atoms and molecules. Yet once complex living things had evolved, and particularly once terrestrial life had become established, its continued existence would have been threatened by high levels of UV radiation (UV causes mutations and biochemical changes at a destructive rate). Ozone cuts off most of the UV radiation which might have been essential for the appearance of life yet harmful to the existence of terrestrial organisms.

3. Blue-green algae, as free-living, self-sufficient phototrophs able to provide their own fixed nitrogen, have acted as 'green manure' to all parts of the Earth's surface that are reasonably damp and moist. The blue-green algal mats of the paddy fields of the tropical and sub-tropical regions maintained soil fertility and permitted the survival of Man long before he was aware of fertilisers, or how plants feed, or of the value of top-dressing crops, i.e. covering the soil surface with manure, with combined nitrogen to maintain the yield under conditions of constant cropping. It has been estimated that 625 g of nitrogen are fixed by blue-green algae per km² annually in the paddy fields of the world. By the steady leaching from cells and on their death and decay, this combined nitrogen is released to other organisms. Blue-green algae increase soil nitrogen, soil humus and the water holding capacity of any soil. Consequently, as early colonisers, they quickly support the vigorous growth of higher plants.

Figure 3.5 View of the ancient mountain-side paddy-fields of the Philippines. These areas have been intensively cropped by Man for around two thousand years. They are just one of the natural environments where blue-green algae are found

Philippine Tourist Agency

Figure 3.6 The place of blue-green algae in the development of the diversity of life

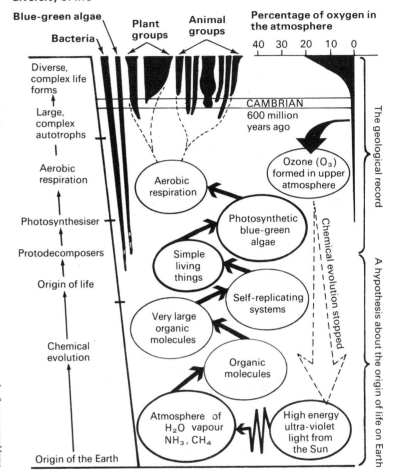

An alternative way prokaryotes capture the Sun's energy

The purple bacterium *Halobacterium halobium* has a unique biochemical mechanism in its plasma membrane for harnessing the energy of the Sun. The organism is halophilic (salt-loving) and occurs naturally in very salty water, e.g. the Dead Sea and certain industrial effluent pools. The cell membrane is covered with purple patches containing a pigment called bacteriorhodopsin. This pigment, when it has associated with it a derivative of vitamin A called retinaldehyde, can trap the energy of sunlight. Light causes physical and chemical changes in the purple patches such that hydrogen ions (protons) are transferred from the inside to the outside of a living cell. The mechanism is known as a proton pump and it sets up a proton electro-chemical gradient across the membrane. This can be demonstrated as a pH difference and as an electrical potential difference between the cell and its medium. This electrical potential represents a form of stored energy. The living cell taps this store as the protons are allowed to flow back into the cell at special sites. Here, Adenosine diphosphate (ADP) and inorganic phosphate (Pi), together with the enzyme ATP-ase, generate Adenosine triphosphate (ATP). (ATP is used by all cells as a source of energy for anabolism, growth and movement.) This unique mechanism of the purple bacterium for harnessing the Sun's energy may have major industrial applications in the future.

Figure 3.7 Diagrammatic representation of a working purple bacterium cell (cell wall omitted)

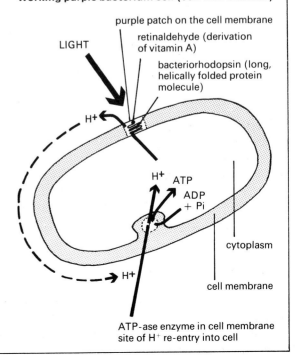

Algae

Algae are eukaryotic, cellular plants with a cell structure very similar to that of higher plants. The group consists of a vast array of photosynthetic organisms, divided by taxonomists into several divisions or phyla, and showing great diversity in plant body, from unicellular or simple filamentous forms to huge seaweeds. Algae live in water, or occasionally they can be found on damp soil or on other moist surfaces. None of the algae, including the huge seaweeds, have special supporting tissues such as fibres. They also have no water-conducting tissue as terrestrial plants do; they live in the totally supportive medium of water. Many unicellular forms are motile, possessing one or more flagella per cell. The gametes of multicellular algae also often have flagella. Cilia and flagella of all eukaryotes have a common structure (see page 27). When undergoing sexual reproduction the whole algal cell may function as a gamete (see page 26), or alternatively gametes may be specially formed in gametangia. Multicellular gametangia consist only of fertile cells; in the algae the gametangium is not surrounded or protected by any sterile cells. Classification of algae is largely based on biochemical evidence, using:

(a) photosynthetic pigments,

(b) food reserves,

and structural features:

(c) cell wall structure,

(d) number and type of flagella (either they are long, whiplash-like or shorter, feathered types), and by the position of the flagella on the cell.

Some divisions within the algae, containing species commonly studied because of their ecological importance, or because of their economic significance

Green algae (*Chlorophyceae*)	Diatoms (*Bacilariophyceae*)
Mainly freshwater aquatic species, or terrestrial in damp conditions. Chlorophylls (*a* and *b*), carotene. Starch and oil food reserves. Cellulose and hemicelluloses in the walls. Flagella: two or four, whiplash, equal in length, anterior attachment. *See pages 22, 26, 28 and 32*	Aquatic and terrestrial in habitat. Chlorophylls (*a* and *c*), carotene, xanthophyll. Fat and leucosin food reserves. Hemicelluloses and silica in the walls. Flagella: only on certain gametes (one flimmer type). *See page 34*
Brown algae (*Phaeophyceae*)	Red algae (*Rhodophyceae*)
Predominantly marine. Chlorophylls (*a* and *c*), carotene and fucoxanthin. Mannitol and laminarin food reserves. Cellulose and hemicelluloses in the walls. Flagella: two unequal length (one whiplash, one flimmer, anterior or lateral). *See page 30*	Mainly marine in habitat. Chlorophylls (*a* and *d*), carotene with phycocyanin and phycoerythrin. Oils and 'floridean' starch (similar to amylopectin) food reserves. No flagella. *See page 32*

Euglenoids

Mainly freshwater in habitat. Containing chlorophylls (*a* and *b*), carotene and xanthophyll. Paramylum food reserves. No cell wall present.
Flagella: maximum of two, only one when it emerges from a gullet. These single-celled organisms are similar to protozoa, and a distinction is sometimes impossible. There are green and colourless forms.

Figure 4.1 Cells from a filament of *Spirogyra* sp. (x500).
The microscope was focused on the mid-line of the cell (optical section), rather than on the outer part of the cell where the chloroplasts are spirally arranged. The drawing shows one cell, enlarged

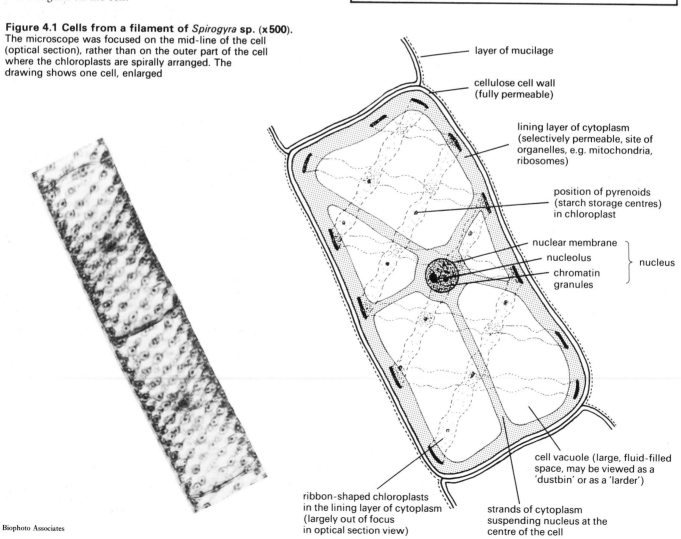

layer of mucilage

cellulose cell wall (fully permeable)

lining layer of cytoplasm (selectively permeable, site of organelles, e.g. mitochondria, ribosomes)

position of pyrenoids (starch storage centres) in chloroplast

nuclear membrane
nucleolus } nucleus
chromatin granules

cell vacuole (large, fluid-filled space, may be viewed as a 'dustbin' or as a 'larder')

ribbon-shaped chloroplasts in the lining layer of cytoplasm (largely out of focus in optical section view)

strands of cytoplasm suspending nucleus at the centre of the cell

Biophoto Associates

The range of vegetative forms within algae

Figure 4.2 *Euglena viridis*, a motile unicellular algae, occurs in stagnant water rich in nitrogenous organic matter (×100)

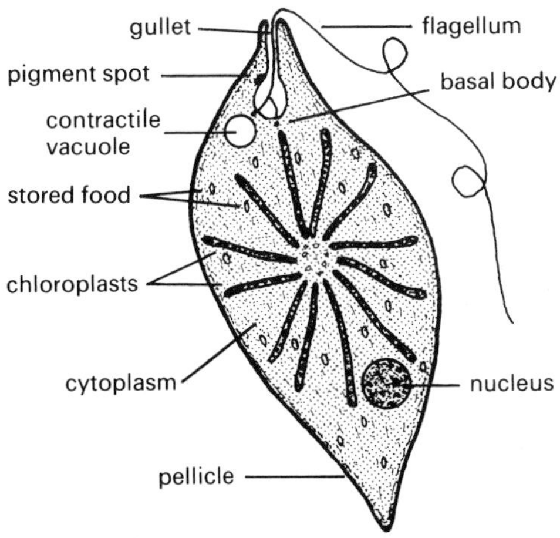

gullet, flagellum, pigment spot, basal body, contractile vacuole, stored food, chloroplasts, cytoplasm, nucleus, pellicle

Motile unicellular forms, e.g. *Chlamydomonas* (see page 26)

Motile colonial forms

Figure 4.4 *Pandorina* sp., 8–32 biflagellate cells embedded in a gelatinous matrix (×700)

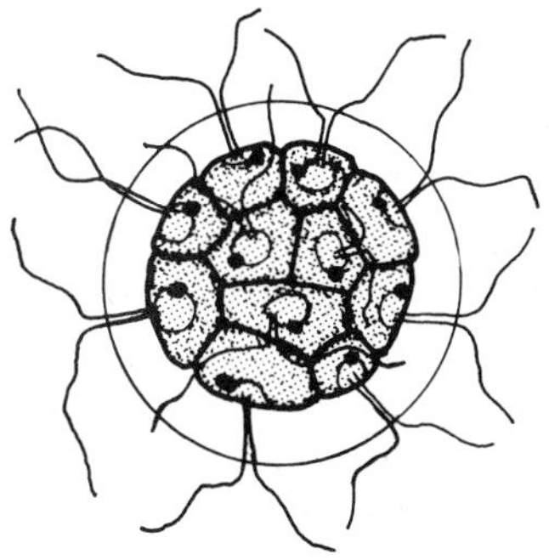

Motionless unicellular forms, e.g. *Chlorella Pleurococcus* (see pages 22 and 23)

Motionless colonial forms

Figure 4.3 *Cladophora* sp. (×50)

Gene Cox

Simple filament forms, e.g. *Spirogyra* (see page 28)

Figure 4.5 Scanning electron micrograph of *Pediastrum* sp. (×500)

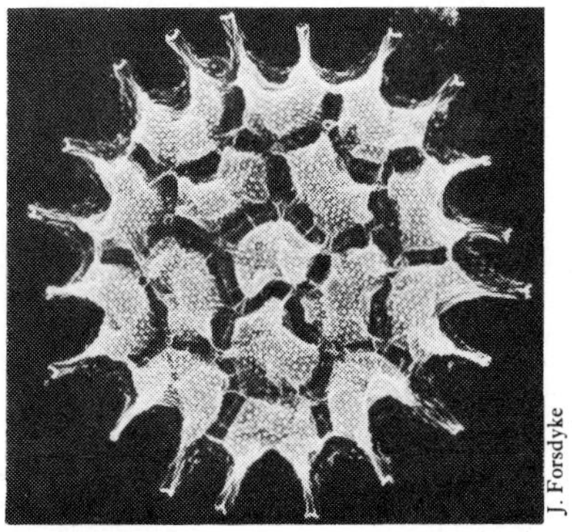

J. Forsdyke

Branched filament forms e.g. *Cladophora*

Thallus forms consist of:
   (i) an aggregation of cells, e.g. Sea Lettuce (*Ulva*) (see page 33),
   (ii) an aggregation of threads, e.g. Wracks (*Fucus*) (see page 30) and Oarweed (*Laminaria*) (below).

Figure 4.6 The Oarweed (*Laminaria digitata***), grows to a length of up to 150 cm**

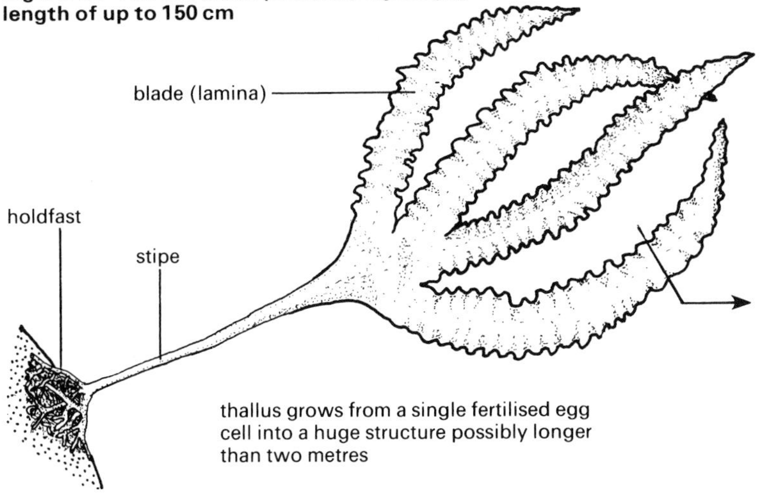

blade (lamina), holdfast, stipe

thallus grows from a single fertilised egg cell into a huge structure possibly longer than two metres

High-powered detail of part of the thallus in section

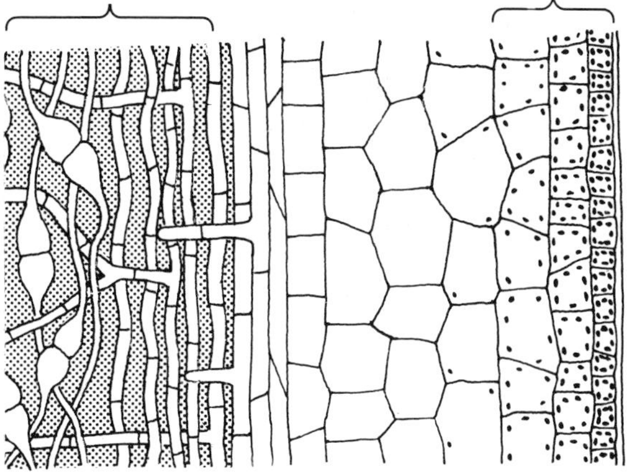

medulla—elongated cells including trumpet hyphae

photosynthetic tissue at the surface

The range of habitats occupied by algae

Open sea (plankton) ⟶ Sea-shore ⟶ Freshwater ⟶ Moist, aerial sites

springs streams rivers   ponds lakes

other plants   rocks   soil

Chlorella

Chlorella vulgaris occurs in freshwater ponds. It grows rapidly, colouring the water bright green, particularly when the pH is slightly alkaline and the water is rich in nutrients from silt and decaying organic matter. The cells are minute green spheres, each with a large, cup-like chloroplast with a pyrenoid (starch storage centre) and colourless, vacuolated cytoplasm with a nucleus. During active growth the cell periodically divides into four protoplasts. These then develop walls, enlarge, and break up the 'mother-cell' wall. This reproduction by asexual formation of autospores is the only form of reproduction that *Chlorella* undergoes.

Chlorella **as an experimental organism**

Chlorella is a popular experimental organism with research biologists. It is easy to maintain in large, uniform populations in confined spaces under rigidly controlled conditions. It has been extensively used in studies of the mechanism of photosynthesis (see page 24), is currently used in investigations of alternative sources of food (single-cell protein studies, see page 49), and it is used in studies of new techniques for harnessing the Sun's energy for fuel and power.

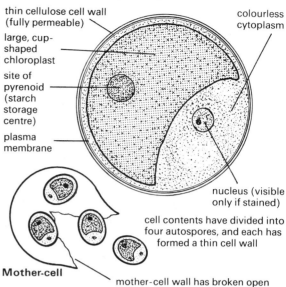

Figure 4.7 *Chlorella vulgaris* **shown fully grown (× 2 500) and at the stage of release of four autospores from the mother-cell wall (× 1 350)**

thin cellulose cell wall (fully permeable)

colourless cytoplasm

large, cup-shaped chloroplast

site of pyrenoid (starch storage centre)

plasma membrane

nucleus (visible only if stained)

cell contents have divided into four autospores, and each has formed a thin cell wall

Mother-cell

mother-cell wall has broken open

Figure 4.8 An experimental set-up for culturing *Chlorella* sp.

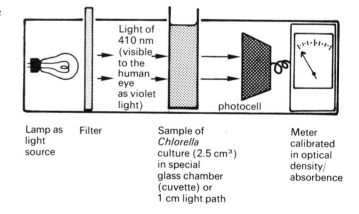

An appropriate nutrient medium to provide the macro-nutrient elements nitrogen, phosphorus, calcium, magnesium, potassium, sulphur, iron and chlorine, and the micro-nutrient elements of boron, cobalt, magnesium, copper, molybdenum, zinc and vanadium at suitable pH, and with the chelating agent sodium EDTA present to hold Fe^{3+} and other trace elements in solution.
(See J. F. Gipps & R. D. Linke 'An experimental system using *Chlorella vulgaris* for population studies in secondary school biology' *J. biol. Ed.* 10 (2) (1976), pp. 87–91.)

fan to prevent overheating due to continuous lighting

glow-lux fluorescent tube

loose plug of non-absorbent cotton wool

50 cm³ medium in a 250 cm³ conical flask at controlled ambient temperature of 25°C

Inoculated with *Chlorella* culture to give an initial concentration of about 20 cells per 0.1 mm³ (this may be estimated by measuring the optical density/absorbence of the suspension)

Stock culture of *Chlorella vulgaris*

Samples are then withdrawn at regular intervals to estimate the population size EITHER by direct counting using a haemocytometer (designed for counting red blood cells, which are a similar size and also non-motile), OR by measuring the increased optical density/absorbence of the sample (due to light absorption and also turbidity) using a colorimeter or spectrophotometer at 410 nm.

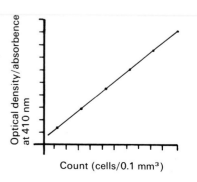

Light of 410 nm (visible to the human eye as violet light)

photocell

Lamp as light source

Filter

Sample of *Chlorella* culture (2.5 cm³) in special glass chamber (cuvette) or 1 cm light path

Meter calibrated in optical density/absorbence

Results

Growth curve for a *Chlorella* culture

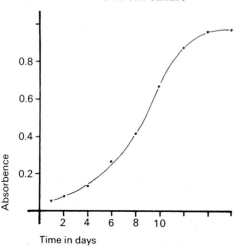

Absorbence

0.8

0.6

0.4

0.2

2   4   6   8   10

Time in days

Calibration curve

There is a linear relationship between the number of cells in a culture (estimated by direct counting of samples) and the optical density/absorbence of the culture (measured by colorimetry/spectrophotometry). Once plotted, the curve of this relationship can be used to convert readings of optical density/absorbence to estimates of the number of *Chlorella* cells in a sample.

Optical density/absorbence at 410 nm

Count (cells/0.1 mm³)

Pleurococcus

Pleurococcus vulgaris is the commonest green alga. It occurs in small aggregations of cells, commonly seen on the windward side of tree trunks, stones, walls and posts. The cells are fairly similar to those of *Chlorella* and they are also non-motile. The chloroplast lines the wall and has a lobed margin; usually there is no pyrenoid. Reproduction occurs only by cell division, and the cells may stick together to some extent. When found submerged underwater (e.g. in a temporary pond in the fork of a tree) more cells remain attached together, forming miniature colonies of up to 50 cells.

Figure 4.9 Drawing of cells of *Pleurococcus* sp. (× 1 500)

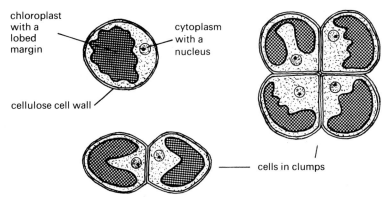

Studying *Pleurococcus* communities in nature

This is a method of estimating the distribution of epiphytic algal colonies around a tree trunk. (Epiphytes are plants that grow on other plants but are not parasitic.)

1. String marked at 5 or 10 cm intervals is secured to the tree trunk at right angles to the earth at a fixed height above the ground (about 1 metre).

2. Starting at magnetic north (using a plotting compass), record the colour density of the *Pleurococcus* colony using your own arbitrary density standard, and repeat at marked intervals.

3. Record also gullies, ponds or waterfall features on the trunk, together with evidence of permanent shading of part of the trunk from neighbouring structures.

4. Set up plastic cups to receive water running off the tree trunk during and following a period of rainfall.

5. Combine the data and results in histograms so that you can speculate on interactions of prevailing winds, sunshine, permanent shadow and running water on the distribution of *Pleurococcus*.

Figure 4.10 A study of *Pleurococcus* distribution and its habitat

1. Density of *Pleurococcus*

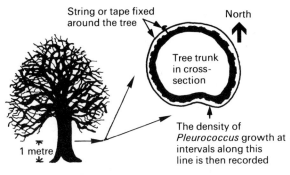

2. Collecting the run-off water around the tree trunk so that it can be measured

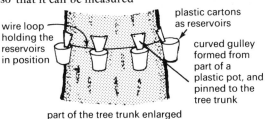

part of the tree trunk enlarged

Colour density scale (arbitrary units) for use in analysing the density of *Pleurococcus* growth on the tree at points around the trunk

Scale	0	1	2	3	4	5
Appearance of the algae:	no visible algal colony	slight	patchy		dark green	intense green, encrustations
Appearance of bark	Clear brown bark					No bark visible

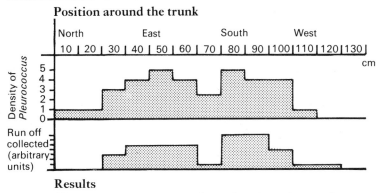

Results

Pleurococcus appears to grow best where it receives moderate sunlight, moisture, humid air, and where it is not exposed to persistent high winds and driving rain.

Finding out about pollution by heavy metal ions and other toxic ions

Toxic ions include those of lead, mercury, cadmium and arsenic. They are present in the Earth's crust but are only very slowly made soluble (mobilised) by natural processes. With the development and growth of the industrial use of metals the exposure of living things to heavy metal ions has significantly increased. They have a permanent denaturing effect on proteins (enzymes), and in lower concentrations they may have other harmful effects (e.g. they displace useful metal ions from metal-containing enzymes causing loss of function).

Investigation of the effect of mercury ions at different concentrations on the growth of *Chlorella* culture, conducted by the technique shown here

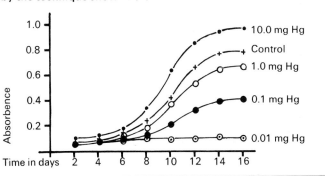

The investigation of photosynthesis

Suspensions of single-celled algae have been used in physiological and biochemical investigations of the process of photosynthesis. Algal cultures are often preferable to whole plants or to pieces of their tissues (called excised tissues and organs) because the diffusion pathway between the external medium and the site of photosynthesis (the chloroplasts) is so short and direct in a unicellular alga, as to be negligible. Any changes made to the medium rapidly become changes at the site of photosynthesis. In contrast, in whole organisms there may be a long and uncertain interval between the supply of substances and their reaching active sites in cells.

1. Early physiological studies

These studies indicated that photosynthesis consists of linked reactions, any one of which may become the main determinant (the limiting factor) of the overall rate.

A simple way of representing photosynthesis is:

Process 1: Light Step

$$\text{LIGHT ENERGY (via chlorophyll)} + H_2O \xrightarrow{\text{photochemical reaction}} \text{REDUCING POWER (H)} + \text{CHEMICAL ENERGY (as ATP)} + O_2 \uparrow$$

Process 2: Dark Step

$$CO_2 + (H) + ATP + \text{ACCEPTOR MOLECULE} \xrightarrow{\text{enzymic reaction}} \text{CARBOHYDRATE}$$

Experiments showed that, for a given light intensity, there is a concentration of carbon dioxide at which all the available light energy is being used. Increasing the concentration of carbon dioxide cannot appreciably increase the rate of photosynthesis; light energy is the limiting factor. Similarly, for a given concentration of carbon dioxide there is a light intensity above which a further increase in light will not appreciably affect the overall rate; carbon dioxide concentration is the limiting factor.

A rise of temperature up to 40°C usually has a stimulatory effect on chemical (and enzymic) processes but much less of an effect on photochemical reactions. The hypothesis that photosynthesis consists of a photochemical step followed by an enzymic reaction was tested with algal cultures. Under low light (photochemical reaction limiting) and then under high light (chemical reaction limiting) the rate of photosynthesis was measured at various temperatures. The results showed that only under high light was temperature rise correlated with increased rate of photosynthesis.

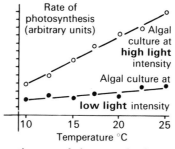

Figure 4.11 The effect of temperature on the rate of photosynthesis at high light (enzymic step is rate-limiting) and at low light (photochemical step is rate-limiting) intensities

2. The production of oxygen by isolated chloroplasts

Experiments with chloroplast preparations from the flowering plants *Stellaria media* and *Lamium album* showed that the photochemical production of oxygen required the presence of suitable hydrogen acceptor and not of carbon dioxide.

Process 1, the Light Step, has come to be known as the Hill Reaction after the first experimenter in this field, Robert Hill.

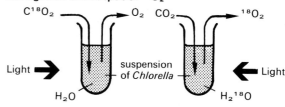

This implies that the traditional balanced equation for photosynthesis:

$$6CO_2 + 6H_2O + \text{LIGHT ENERGY} \xrightarrow{\substack{\text{chlorophyll} \\ \text{pigments in} \\ \text{chloroplast}}} C_6H_{12}O_6 + 6O_2 \uparrow$$

is incorrect in suggesting that some or all of the oxygen evolved comes from carbon dioxide. Experiments with the non-radioactive isotope ^{18}O ('heavy' oxygen has to be detected with the mass spectrometer) and experiments with cultures of *Chlorella*, have confirmed that the oxygen evolved in photosynthesis comes from water only.

Figure 4.12 The effect of supplying either carbon dioxide or water containing ^{18}O to *Chlorella* cells in the light on the output of $^{18}O_2$

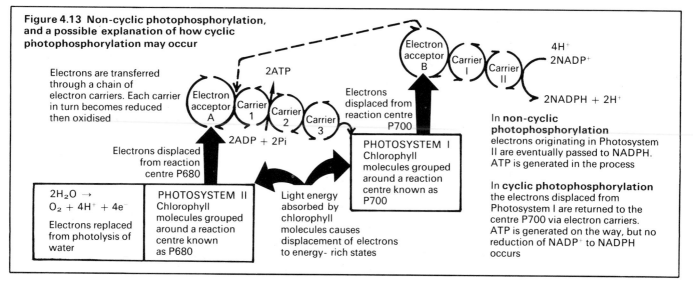

The equation for photosynthesis is less misleading when written as:

$$6CO_2 + 12H_2O + \text{LIGHT ENERGY} \rightarrow C_6H_{12}O_6 + 6O_2 \uparrow + 6H_2O$$

It has also been shown that in the light reaction adenosine triphosphate (ATP) is formed from adenosine diphosphate (ADP) and phosphate ions by two processes called respectively cyclic photophosphorylation and non-cyclic photophosphorylation.

Figure 4.13 Non-cyclic photophosphorylation, and a possible explanation of how cyclic photophosphorylation may occur

Electrons are transferred through a chain of electron carriers. Each carrier in turn becomes reduced then oxidised

Electrons displaced from reaction centre P680

$$2H_2O \rightarrow O_2 + 4H^+ + 4e^-$$

Electrons replaced from photolysis of water

PHOTOSYSTEM II Chlorophyll molecules grouped around a reaction centre known as P680

Light energy absorbed by chlorophyll molecules causes displacement of electrons to energy-rich states

Electrons displaced from reaction centre P700

PHOTOSYSTEM I Chlorophyll molecules grouped around a reaction centre known as P700

In **non-cyclic photophosphorylation** electrons originating in Photosystem II are eventually passed to NADPH. ATP is generated in the process

In **cyclic photophosphorylation** the electrons displaced from Photosystem I are returned to the centre P700 via electron carriers. ATP is generated on the way, but no reduction of NADP$^+$ to NADPH occurs

3. The path of carbon in photosynthesis

The pathway of carbon from carbon dioxide into the large biochemical molecules of the green cell was investigated using radioactively labelled carbon dioxide ($^{14}CO_2$) fed to illuminated cultures of *Chlorella*. The experiments, pioneered by Melvin Calvin at the University of California, established that the initial product of fixation of carbon dioxide was phosphoglyceraldehyde (PGA), the acceptor molecule was ribulose diphosphate, and the initial products of photosynthesis (sugars) were rapidly metabolised into organic acids, amino acids and fatty acids. Fresh samples of the experimental culture were run-off at regular intervals (e.g. 5 seconds) after a pulse of $^{14}CO_2$ had been fed to the culture. Alcohol was used to kill the cells and extract the metabolites. These were then separated by chromatography.

Figure 4.14 Melvin Calvin's 'lollipop' apparatus and experimental procedure

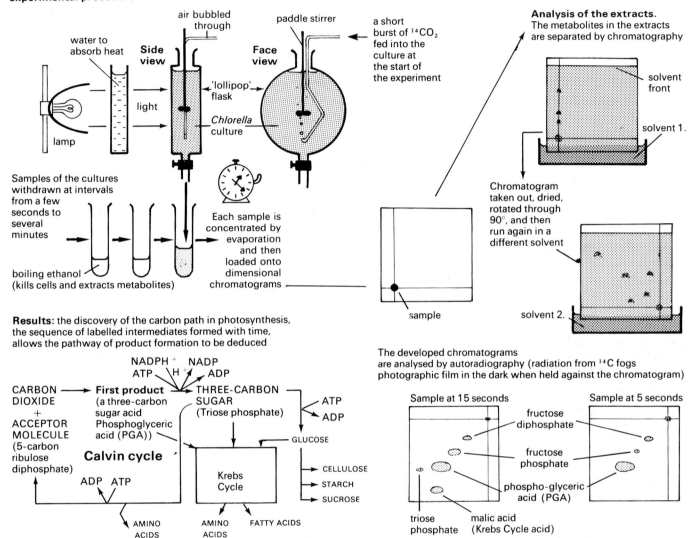

Figure 4.15 Summary of the process and siting of the light and dark steps of photosynthesis in the chloroplast

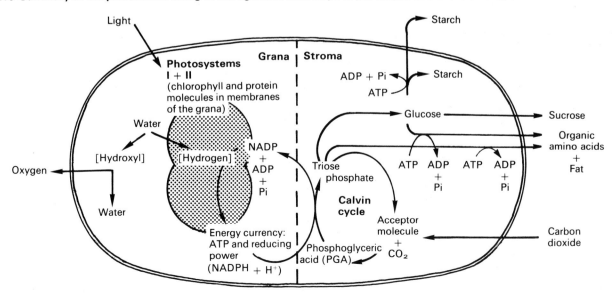

The alga *Chlamydomonas*

Chlamydomonas, a genus of freshwater alga, is common in ponds contaminated with ammonium compounds. There are about 400 different species. They are small, motile, unicellular plants that move by the rapid beating of the two flagella that protrude through the thin cellulose wall at the anterior (pointed) end. They feed by photosynthesis and by metabolising the sugar produced to synthesise all their other requirements, using ions taken from the pond water. They have a brightly coloured eyespot which is believed to be sensitive to light intensity and to the direction from which the incident light comes. They also have two contractile vacuoles in which excess water, brought in by osmosis, collects and is discharged through the cell walls to the outside.

Figure 4.16 *Chlamydomonas* **sp. in pond water, observed by phase-contrast microscopy (× 650)**

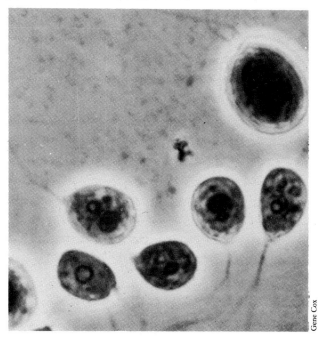

Gene Cox

Figure 4.17 A summary of the life-cycle of *Chlamydomonas*

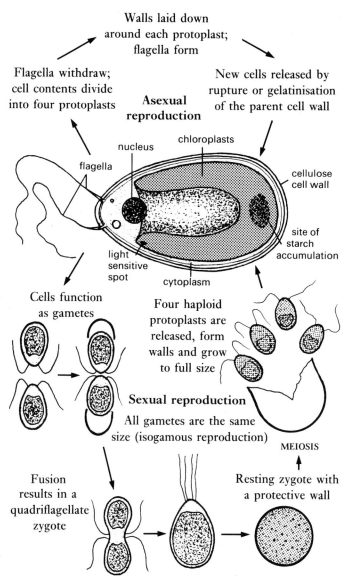

Walls laid down around each protoplast; flagella form

Flagella withdraw; cell contents divide into four protoplasts

Asexual reproduction

New cells released by rupture or gelatinisation of the parent cell wall

nucleus

chloroplasts

flagella

cellulose cell wall

site of starch accumulation

light sensitive spot

cytoplasm

Cells function as gametes

Four haploid protoplasts are released, form walls and grow to full size

Sexual reproduction

All gametes are the same size (isogamous reproduction)

MEIOSIS

Fusion results in a quadriflagellate zygote

Resting zygote with a protective wall

Figure 4.18(i) Electron micrograph of a longitudinal section of *Chlamydomonas* **sp. cut just to one side of the median line (flagella not visible in the plane of section) (× 10 500)**

Figure 4.18(ii) Drawing of the cell structure of *Chlamydomonas* **sp. shown by electron microscopy**

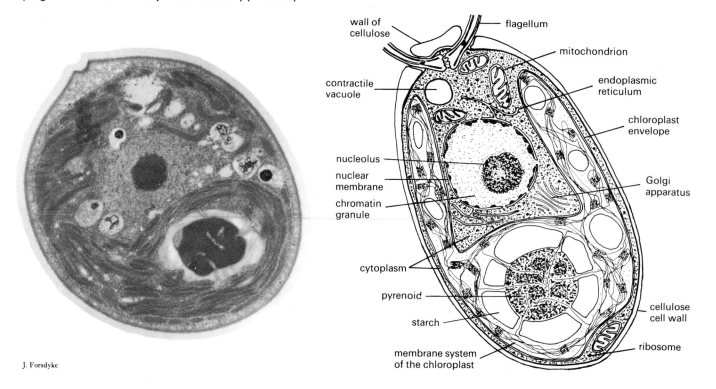

J. Forsdyke

wall of cellulose

flagellum

mitochondrion

contractile vacuole

endoplasmic reticulum

chloroplast envelope

nucleolus

nuclear membrane

chromatin granule

Golgi apparatus

cytoplasm

pyrenoid

starch

cellulose cell wall

ribosome

membrane system of the chloroplast

Cilia and flagella

Cilia and flagella are organelles which project from the surface of a wide range of eukaryotic cells. Flagella occur in small numbers on small cells, cilia in large numbers on larger cells. They are structurally almost identical, but are distinguished by their behaviour as well as their relative size.

Flagella are usually found singly or in pairs.

A single flagellum (e.g. a sperm) beats with a sine wave motion, travelling from base to tip. This causes water to be pushed along the flagellum.

Two flagella (e.g. *Chlamydomonas*) beat laterally, drawing water past the organism.

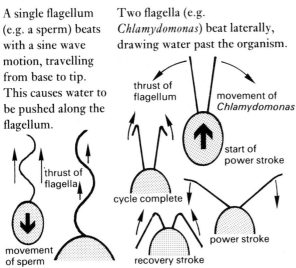

Cilia occur in large numbers lining specific cells, e.g. *Paramecium* and cells of the human bronchus. They beat asymmetrically with a stiff propulsion stroke followed by a flexible recovery stroke.

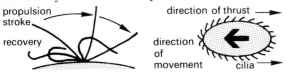

Motile colonial forms

Volvox is a green, spherical, hollow colony ranging from 500 to 60 000 chlamydomonas-like cells supported in a gelatinous matrix. The cells are joined by cytoplasmic strands, and each cell is biflagellate. All cells of the colony appear identical but there is marked polarity in the colony. During movement, one point on the sphere is always anterior, and the whole colony's flagella movements must co-ordinate to achieve this. Only a restricted number of cells at the posterior part of the colony are capable of reproduction. In asexual reproduction a small sphere of cells is formed in the inside of the colony. This sphere either escapes later through a small pore in the parent colony, or it remains until the parent dies and disintegrates. Several daughter colonies can be seen in a fully grown *Volvox* colony.

Sexual reproduction also occurs. Female gametes develop from vegetative cells without division, and these are termed oogonia. As each oogonium enlarges it loses its flagella and acquires a large food store around the pyrenoid. Male gametes are formed by repeated division of vegetative cells, and these are termed antherozoids. One cell may form more than 500 tiny, motile antherozoids. This specialisation of male and female gametes, in terms of their size and behaviour is called oogamous reproduction. It contrasts with isogamous reproduction shown in the life cycle of *Chlamydomonas*.

The structure of cilia and flagella

Cilia and flagella have a structure of 9 pairs of peripheral microtubules and 2 central microtubules running their length, surrounded by plasma membrane and held together with proteinaceous links. The structure is firmly anchored in the cell by the basal body.

Figure 4.19 Electron micrograph of a flagellum, viewed in transverse section (x200 000). The accompanying line drawing shows the complex pattern of the microtubules and protein membranes which are believed to make up the structure of this organelle

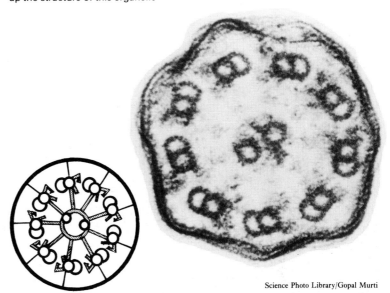

Science Photo Library/Gopal Murti

The mechanism of beating of cilia and flagella

This is not understood, but when their shaft is removed from the cell (severed from the basal body) it may continue to beat. It may be that protein from the membranes linking the microtubules are enzymes that can release energy from ATP to cause selected microtubules to slide past each other.

Figure 4.20 *Volvox* **colonies showing daughter colonies inside each sphere, formed by asexual reproduction (× 350)**

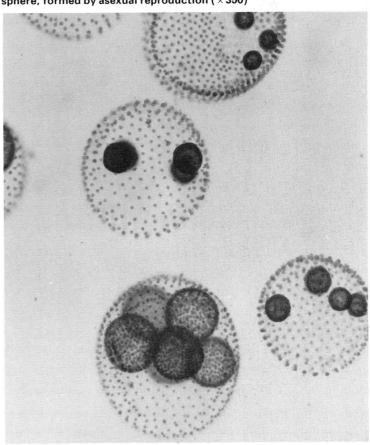

Gene Cox

The alga *Spirogyra*

Spirogyra is an exceedingly common alga in stagnant ponds in spring. It also occurs in lakes attached to rocks by a holdfast cell (this is the first or basal cell in a filament, modified to grip onto a rock or a stone). The holdfast is strong enough to keep the whole filament attached to stones in freshwater streams where it also occurs. *Spirogyra* frequently has diatoms (see page 34) associated with it, growing as epiphytes along the filament. The filament is unbranched and is slimy to the touch. The layer of mucilage that lines the outside of the filament often holds filaments together in a matted blanket. Bubbles of gas (mostly oxygen given off in the light from photosynthesis) can become trapped below these filaments and support the mass of *Spirogyra* at the pond surface. The chloroplast (or chloroplasts; there may be up to seven per cell) is ribbon-shaped with wavy or even jagged edges. The chloroplast is helically coiled in the layer of cytoplasm lining the long cell wall.

Figure 4.21 Part of a filament of *Spirogyra* sp. The cellulose wall forms a strong cylinder, but the cells can become kinked and broken, and the filament fragmented (× 400)

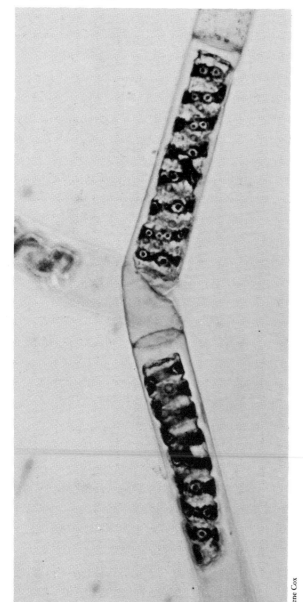

Gene Cox

Figure 4.22 The structure and physiology of the *Spirogyra* cell

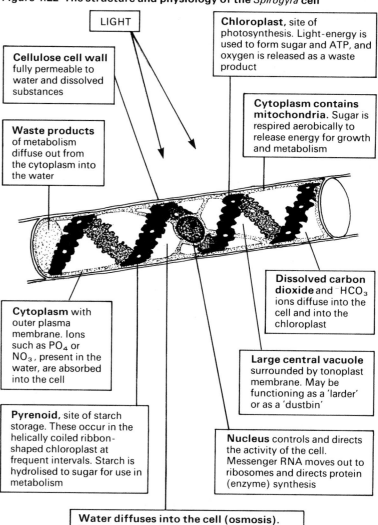

LIGHT

Cellulose cell wall fully permeable to water and dissolved substances

Chloroplast, site of photosynthesis. Light-energy is used to form sugar and ATP, and oxygen is released as a waste product

Cytoplasm contains mitochondria. Sugar is respired aerobically to release energy for growth and metabolism

Waste products of metabolism diffuse out from the cytoplasm into the water

Dissolved carbon dioxide and HCO_3^- ions diffuse into the cell and into the chloroplast

Cytoplasm with outer plasma membrane. Ions such as PO_4 or NO_3, present in the water, are absorbed into the cell

Large central vacuole surrounded by tonoplast membrane. May be functioning as a 'larder' or as a 'dustbin'

Pyrenoid, site of starch storage. These occur in the helically coiled ribbon-shaped chloroplast at frequent intervals. Starch is hydrolised to sugar for use in metabolism

Nucleus controls and directs the activity of the cell. Messenger RNA moves out to ribosomes and directs protein (enzyme) synthesis

Water diffuses into the cell (osmosis). Excess water uptake is prevented by hydrostatic pressure due to the firm cell wall. The cell sap is of greater osmotic potential (has higher solute concentration) than the pond water

Figure 4.23(i) Drawing of stages in the process of sexual reproduction by conjugation in *Spirogyra* sp. (× 570)

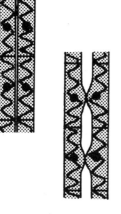

1. Adjacent filaments held together by the mucilage layers

2. A conjugation tube between cells is formed by simultaneous outgrowth of the walls, forcing the filament apart

3. The end walls of the opposing tubes break down; the conjugation tube is complete

4. Protoplasts from the cells of one filament migrate into the cells of the other filament

6. The zygotes lay down protective walls and become zygospores

5. A zygote is formed when the nuclei fuse in each cell

Figure 4.23(ii) Structure and germination of the zygospores

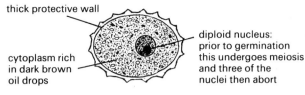
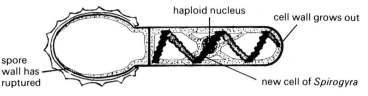

Figure 4.24 Phase-contrast photomicrograph of conjugating *Spirogyra* **filaments at the moment of protoplast migration and formation of the zygote (×400)**

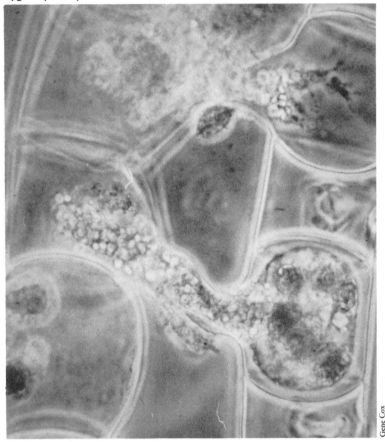

Gene Cox

Figure 4.25 Zygospores of *Spirogyra* **sp. showing the thick protective walls surrounding the zygotes (×1200).** The cell contents of each cell pair have acted as a gamete; all the contents of one filament (behaving as the female gametes) through the conjugation tube. The zygospores are released only on decay of the old filament cell wall

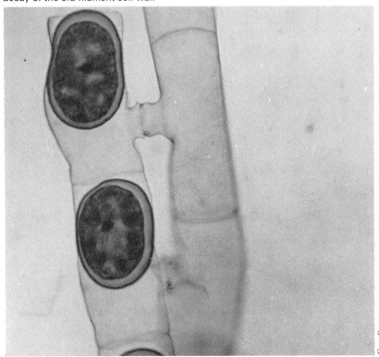

Gene Cox

Life-cycle of *Spirogyra*

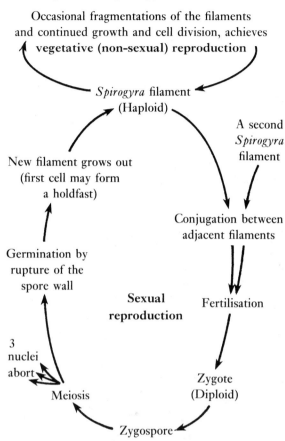

Spirogyra is just one of three or four commonly occurring unbranched filamentous algae that form conspicuous floating masses in pond water. These green algae can be identified or differentiated by examination under the microscope; the chloroplasts are of easily distinguished shapes.

Zygnema has two star-shaped chloroplasts in each cell.

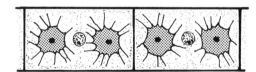

Ulothrix has a single girdle-shaped chloroplast in each cell.

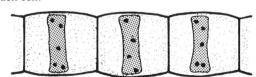

Mougeotia cells each have a thin, flat, centrally placed chloroplast with numerous pyrenoids.

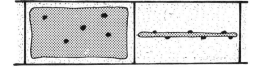

Wracks (*Fucus*)

Fucus is a genus of cold-water marine algae, common around the coasts of Europe, North America and parts of Asia. Several species grow in profusion anchored to rocks in the inter-tidal zone of the shore. The plants are adapted to withstand the limited exposure and mild desiccation that occurs between high-tides.

The plant body (thallus) has a disc-shaped holdfast (hapteron) which grips the irregular surface of rock or breakwater structures, making it very difficult to dislodge. The stalk (stipe) extends as the mid-rib and supports the broad, ribbon-shaped blade (lamina). The thallus divides into each branch (dichotomous branching) from time to time as it grows, forming a new mid-rib and blade. The whole structure is slippery, tough and almost leathery, making *Fucus* fairly resistant to wave damage. Cells of the thallus can grow and divide, and damage to the thallus can be repaired by regenerative growth. The film of mucilage that originates in the tiny pits (conceptacles) all over the plant body, also reduces water loss from the thallus during periods of exposure to hot sunshine and dry winds.

Figure 4.26 Drawing showing the vegetative structure of *Fucus* sp.

plant body called a thallus { holdfast (hapteron) / stalk (stipe) / blade (lamina)

rock

sterile conceptacles occur all over the plant. From these tiny pits comes the mucilage that covers the surface of the whole thallus (see below)

Line of VS of the tip of the fertile frond, shown in figure 4.27

mid-rib

thallus branches dichotomously

tip of thallus becomes swollen with conspicuous fertile conceptacles (these contain the reproductive organs)

Figure 4.27 Section through a receptacle of *Fucus vesiculosus* showing the large, spherical, fertile conceptacles. Each conceptacle opens to the surface through a narrow hole (ostiole). Mucilage and gametes are formed inside the conceptacle, and are released into the sea through the ostiole

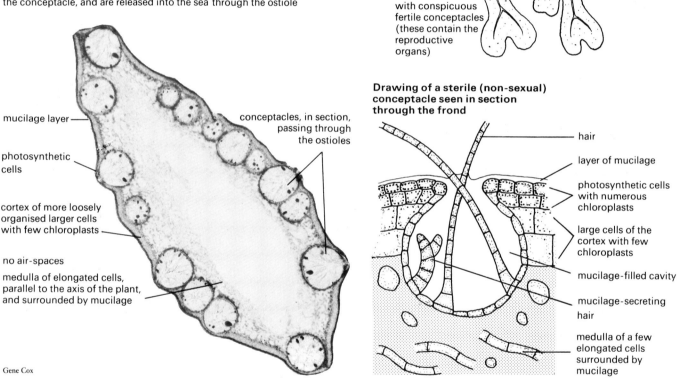

mucilage layer

photosynthetic cells

cortex of more loosely organised larger cells with few chloroplasts

no air-spaces

medulla of elongated cells, parallel to the axis of the plant, and surrounded by mucilage

conceptacles, in section, passing through the ostioles

Gene Cox

Drawing of a sterile (non-sexual) conceptacle seen in section through the frond

hair

layer of mucilage

photosynthetic cells with numerous chloroplasts

large cells of the cortex with few chloroplasts

mucilage-filled cavity

mucilage-secreting hair

medulla of a few elongated cells surrounded by mucilage

Three common species of *Fucus*

Serrated Wrack (*F. serratus*) has a serrated edge to the thallus; grows up to 60 cm

Bladder Wrack (*F. vesiculosus*) has a prominent mid-rib with numerous air bladders, commonly in pairs, in the thallus; grows up to 1 m

Flat Wrack (*F. spiralis*) has a broad thallus that is slightly spirally twisted; grows up to 1.5 m

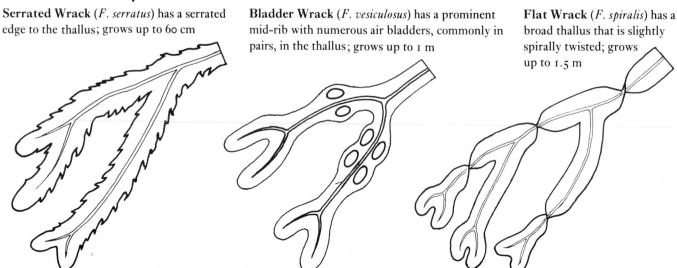

Sexual reproduction in *Fucus*

Gametes are formed in fertile conceptacles that occur in conspicuously swollen tips of the thallus. In two species conceptacles are either male or female, not both. The ova (female gametes) are relatively large and non-motile. Eight ova are formed in the female sex organ (an oogonium), and many oogonia develop in each female conceptacle. The antherozoids (male gametes) are small and motile. Sixty-four antherozoids are formed in the male sex organ (an antheridium), and many thousands of antheridia develop in each male conceptacle. Meiosis occurs during gamete formation. The gametes are only formed during particular seasons (usually autumn or spring around British coasts) and are released at low tides. During these periods of exposure to the air the thallus dries slightly causing some contraction of the tissue and the squeezing out of mucilage and packets of gametes. On the return of the tide the gametes are released by gelatinisation of the packet walls on contact with sea water. Fertilisation occurs in the water.

In *F. serratus* and *F. vesiculosus*, each plant is unisexual. The plants bear either male conceptacles or female conceptacles. In *F. spiralis*, ova and antheridia are produced on the same plant and often with antheridia and oogonia in the same conceptacle (hermaphrodite).

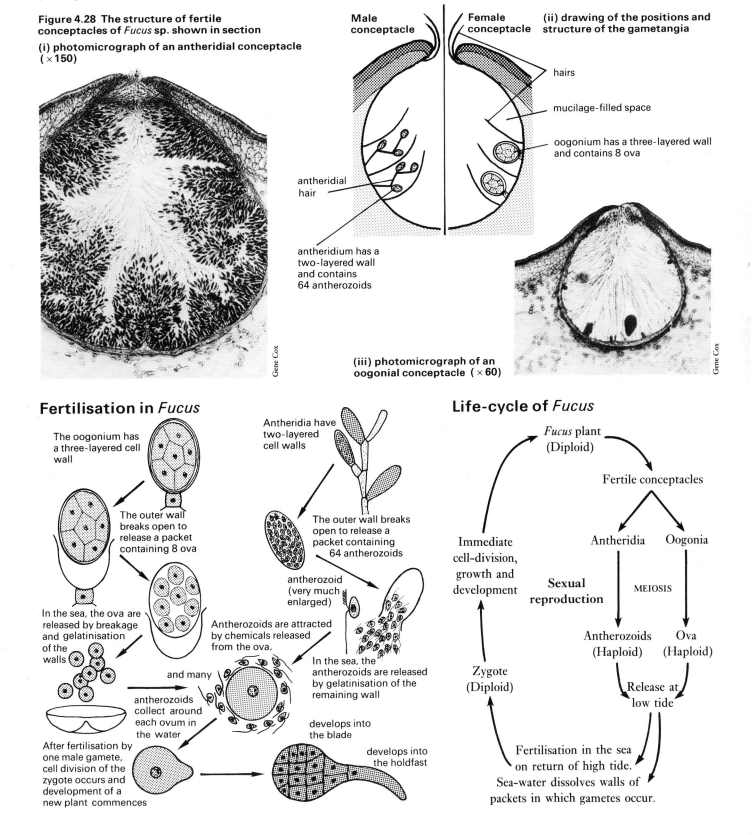

Figure 4.28 The structure of fertile conceptacles of *Fucus* sp. shown in section

(i) photomicrograph of an antheridial conceptacle (×150)

Male conceptacle

Female conceptacle

(ii) drawing of the positions and structure of the gametangia

hairs

mucilage-filled space

oogonium has a three-layered wall and contains 8 ova

antheridial hair

antheridium has a two-layered wall and contains 64 antherozoids

(iii) photomicrograph of an oogonial conceptacle (×60)

Fertilisation in *Fucus*

The oogonium has a three-layered cell wall

The outer wall breaks open to release a packet containing 8 ova

In the sea, the ova are released by breakage and gelatinisation of the walls

and many antherozoids collect around each ovum in the water

After fertilisation by one male gamete, cell division of the zygote occurs and development of a new plant commences

Antheridia have two-layered cell walls

The outer wall breaks open to release a packet containing 64 antherozoids

antherozoid (very much enlarged)

Antherozoids are attracted by chemicals released from the ova,

In the sea, the antherozoids are released by gelatinisation of the remaining wall

develops into the blade

develops into the holdfast

Life-cycle of *Fucus*

Fucus plant (Diploid)

Fertile conceptacles

Immediate cell-division, growth and development

Sexual reproduction

Antheridia   Oogonia

MEIOSIS

Antherozoids (Haploid)   Ova (Haploid)

Release at low tide

Zygote (Diploid)

Fertilisation in the sea on return of high tide. Sea-water dissolves walls of packets in which gametes occur.

The shore as a habitat

The shore can contain an enormous variety of substrata, from rock or pebbles, to sand or mud-flats. The action of the special features of tides and waves on the sloping shore create a distinct zonation in both the physical environment and in the population of plants and animals that live between the high- and low-water marks.

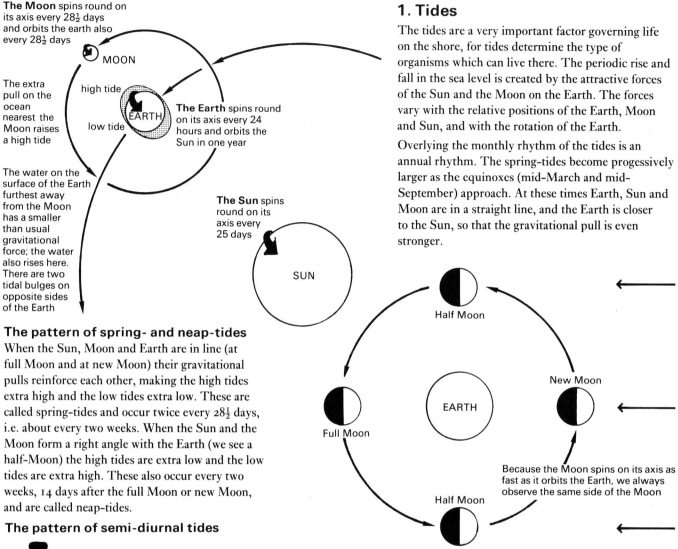

The **Moon** spins round on its axis every $28\frac{1}{2}$ days and orbits the earth also every $28\frac{1}{2}$ days

The extra pull on the ocean nearest the Moon raises a high tide

high tide

low tide

MOON

EARTH

The Earth spins round on its axis every 24 hours and orbits the Sun in one year

The water on the surface of the Earth furthest away from the Moon has a smaller than usual gravitational force; the water also rises here. There are two tidal bulges on opposite sides of the Earth

The Sun spins round on its axis every 25 days

SUN

The pattern of spring- and neap-tides

When the Sun, Moon and Earth are in line (at full Moon and at new Moon) their gravitational pulls reinforce each other, making the high tides extra high and the low tides extra low. These are called spring-tides and occur twice every $28\frac{1}{2}$ days, i.e. about every two weeks. When the Sun and the Moon form a right angle with the Earth (we see a half-Moon) the high tides are extra low and the low tides are extra high. These also occur every two weeks, 14 days after the full Moon or new Moon, and are called neap-tides.

The pattern of semi-diurnal tides

High-water (spring-tide)

High-water (neap-tide)

Tidal range of spring-tides

Tidal range of neap-tides

Low-water (neap-tide) (LWN)

Low-water (spring-tide) (LWS)

rock uncovered at LWS but not at LWN

As the Earth rotates in relation to the Moon every 24 hours, in most places high tides occur approximately every 12 hours (half-daily). These are known as the semi-diurnal tides. Most of Britain has this semi-diurnal tide pattern. Other factors can alter this 12-hourly cycle; for example, on the South Coast between Portland and Portsmouth there are double tides every 24 hours, due to the proximity of the Isle of Wight, called quarterly diurnal tides.

1. Tides

The tides are a very important factor governing life on the shore, for tides determine the type of organisms which can live there. The periodic rise and fall in the sea level is created by the attractive forces of the Sun and the Moon on the Earth. The forces vary with the relative positions of the Earth, Moon and Sun, and with the rotation of the Earth.

Overlying the monthly rhythm of the tides is an annual rhythm. The spring-tides become progessively larger as the equinoxes (mid-March and mid-September) approach. At these times Earth, Sun and Moon are in a straight line, and the Earth is closer to the Sun, so that the gravitational pull is even stronger.

Half Moon

New Moon

EARTH

Full Moon

Half Moon

Because the Moon spins on its axis as fast as it orbits the Earth, we always observe the same side of the Moon

2. Waves

Anything that disturbs the surface of the water will cause a wave, but most waves are caused by wind. The uninterrupted distance over which a wind builds up a wave is known as the fetch. (A westerly gale blowing on Cornwall may have a fetch of more than a thousand miles and can raise a ferocious sea.) Once generated a wave runs on under its own momentum and may travel huge distances, unless opposed by wind. Waves of different origins combine together and give the uneven pattern often observed on shore. As waves come to shallow water they slow down, come closer together, and are made steeper. Then as the water is slowed down by the shore the waves spill over and plunge onto the land. The breaking wave is a grinding mill, pounding and tearing at rocks, pebbles and sand, and at the anchored and moving life. It scatters sea-water over organisms, about and above the tide line in the area called the splash zone.

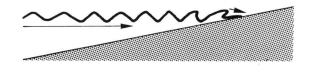

Zonation

The tide imposes alternate periods of submersion and emersion. The contrast between these conditions is extreme, and persists for longer periods the higher one goes up the shore. These differences are the basis of the zonation.

Submersion	Emersion
Temperature is uniform.	Temperature changes are enormous.
There is no water loss problem.	Desiccation is a major danger.
Water contains dissolved O_2, CO_2, inorganic ions and organic debris.	Heavy rain can cause sudden salinity changes.
There is a danger of dislodgement by waves, as the tide covers the land.	
There is danger of predation from sea organisms.	
Light penetration to lower levels is reduced.	

The animals and plants of the shore are almost all of marine origin, but there are quite clearly defined belts or zones of different kinds of organisms between high- and low-water marks, running parallel to the sea. This zonation reflects differing capacity of organisms to withstand prolonged exposure higher up the shore-line, and also the differing ability of seaweeds to photosynthesise adequately using only the blue-green wavelengths of light that can penetrate deeper water, near the low-water mark. The seaweeds are the major primary producers of the shore zone, and they also provide cover and protection for much of the animal life.

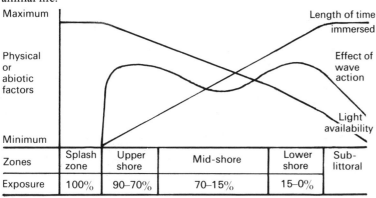

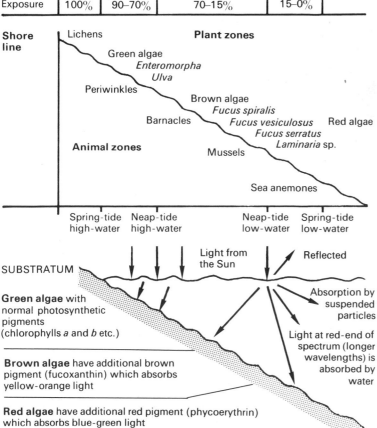

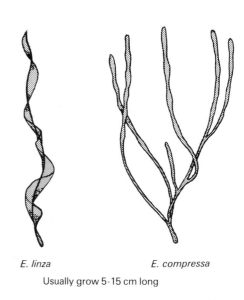

Figure 4.29 Green algae of the upper shore
Enteromorpha sp.

E. linza   E. compressa
Usually grow 5-15 cm long

The Sea-Lettuce *Ulva* sp.

Thallus in section (2-cells thick)

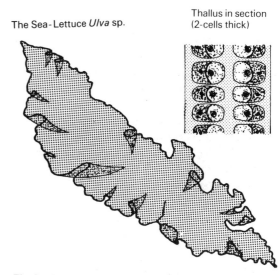

The Sea-Lettuce (*Ulva* sp.) grows 10-20 cm long

Red algae of the lower shore

Figure 4.30 Common red algae

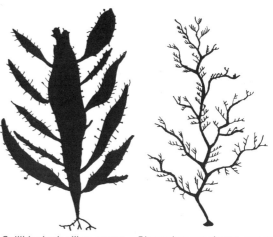

Calliblepharis ciliata, grows up to 15 cm

Plocamium coccineum, grows up to 15 cm

Diatoms

Diatoms occur in all habitats; marine, freshwater, the soil and on other plants, but most of all they make up the marine and freshwater plankton. Plankton is of fundamental ecological importance as the major primary producer in the food-webs of the open ocean and of freshwaters (see facing page).

Diatoms are single-celled algae with a unique cell wall structure. Their cells have walls of two overlapping portions called valves, one slightly larger than the other.

Figure 4.32 Drawing of a diatom seen in section

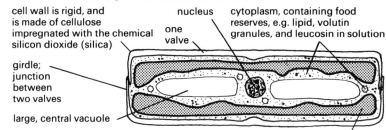

cell wall is rigid, and is made of cellulose impregnated with the chemical silicon dioxide (silica)

girdle; junction between two valves

large, central vacuole

nucleus

one valve

cytoplasm, containing food reserves, e.g. lipid, volutin granules, and leucosin in solution

chloroplasts are yellow-brown in colour, containing the photosynthetic pigments chlorophylls, carotene and fucoxanthin; they are either large and lobed, as shown here, or they may possess many discoid chloroplasts

The two basic shapes of diatoms

1. Radially symmetrical (centric) diatoms are shaped like a circular box or a Petri dish, and are circular or triangle-shaped in valve view.

Valve view

Arachnodiscus sp.   *Lithodesmium* sp.

Girdle view

2. Bilaterally symmetrical (pennate) diatoms are shaped like a date box, and are narrow and elongated in valve view.

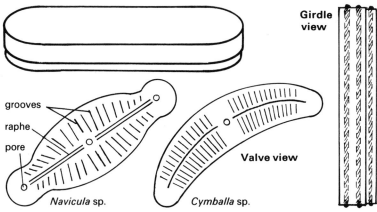

Girdle view

grooves

raphe

pore

Valve view

Navicula sp.   *Cymballa* sp.

Surface patterning on the valves is often very complex, consisting of pores, raised areas and grooves.

Figure 4.33 Scanning electron micrograph of the diatom *Navicula* sp. showing the raphe and grooves on the valve and the various bands of thickening on the girdle view, including the central band at the junction between the two halves of the cell wall (×12 000)

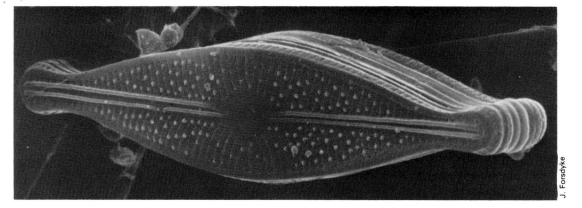

J. Forsdyke

The diatom cell wall and fossil diatoms

When aquatic diatoms die they sink to the bottom and the protoplasts disintegrate leaving the silica-impregnated walls as instant fossils. Huge deposits of these, known as diatomaceous earth, have accumulated in earlier geological periods (see page 36).

Movement

Many of the pennate diatoms make small jerky movements. This may be achieved by the friction between streaming of mucilage in the long central groove of the valve and the surrounding water.

the central groove is called the raphe: along this groove the mucilage flows

raphe

Growth and reproduction

Reproduction is mostly by cell division.

The effect of repeated division of this type is that the cells get progressively smaller. Periodically the cell contents form a spore (called an auxospore) and the existing valves are discarded. Eventually the spore grows into a diatom with new large valves. (Sometimes the auxospores are formed as a result of fusion of two diatom cell protoplasts, i.e. sexual reproduction.)

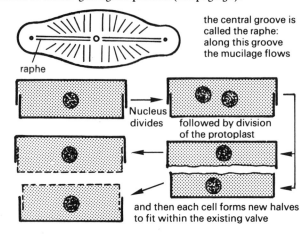

Nucleus divides

followed by division of the protoplast

and then each cell forms new halves to fit within the existing valve

Phytoplankton and aquatic food-webs

Plankton consists of tiny plants (phytoplankton) and animals
(zooplankton) that float passively or move slowly in the surface layers
of natural waters. Phytoplankton are photosynthetic; zooplankton feed
on the phytoplankton. The greater part of the Earth's surface is covered
with water. The total area of ocean alone is 361 700 000 km² (71% of
the Earth's surface). This being the case, photosynthesis by aquatic
plants and the cycling of aquatic food webs are of the greatest
significance in the balance of nature.

A generalised aquatic food-web

The names of specific organisms can be added for any particular aquatic
habitat being studied.

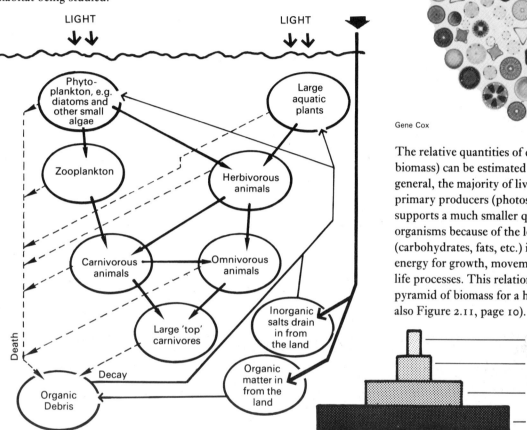

**Figure 4.34 Photomicrograph of a selection of
diatoms on a microscope slide (× 20).** The patterns on
the valves (due to the grooves, ridges and pores) have been
highlighted by cleaning dead diatoms with an oxidising
agent to remove organic cell contents leaving only the
sculptured cell walls

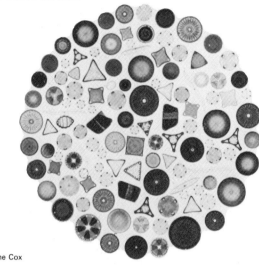

Gene Cox

The relative quantities of different organisms (their
biomass) can be estimated for a particular habitat. In
general, the majority of living material exists as the
primary producers (photosynthetic organisms) and
supports a much smaller quantity of consumer
organisms because of the loss of substance
(carbohydrates, fats, etc.) in respiration to release
energy for growth, movement, reproduction, and all
life processes. This relationship is expressed in a
pyramid of biomass for a habitat or a food-web (see
also Figure 2.11, page 10).

Tertiary consumers:
the few top carnivores

Secondary consumers:
large carnivores and omnivores

Primary consumers:
the herbivorous animals
and zooplankton

Primary producers:
the photosynthetic plants

Man's exploitation of the sea

1. The sea as a source of food

About 80% of our marine harvest of fish comes from quite restricted areas of the oceans. These are close to continents where the
sea bed falls away precipitously and where strong and persistent winds move surface water away and draw up water from the
depths. This 'upwelling' of water brings up nutrients released from accumulated dead organic matter by decay. These nutrients
are natural fertilisers for the phytoplankton. Upwelling by the Peru current off South America produces one of the richest
fishing areas in the world. The annual world harvest of fish (this comes largely from the sea) is rising, yet the yield per unit area
of ocean is low in comparison with animal husbandry on the land. The extent to which the naturally produced food from the sea
can be increased is at present, uncertain. Today only 50% of the fish harvest is eaten by humans, the remainder is used for
feeding livestock.

2. The oceans as a safe dustbin

The great area and depth of the world's oceans may suggest to Man that these are the safest dustbin in which to bury concentrated
poisonous waste from industry and from extraction processes. The chemicals that are disposed of include:

(a) toxins that are only very slowly decayed by bacteria, e.g. tetrachlorodibenzo-*para*-dioxin (TCDD) or Dioxin;

(b) radioactive isotopes, e.g. carbon 14 (half-life of 5 800 years), which can substitute for carbon 12 in fats, proteins, etc., and
strontium 90 (half-life of 28 years), which can substitute for calcium in bones and shells;

(c) concentrated waste containing heavy metal ions, e.g. lead ions, an accumulative poison of the central nervous system.

The steady accumulation of toxic substances in the seas and any dumping of such very toxic waste at great depths in the ocean, poses
a long-term threat to all living things. The corrosive action of the sea on containers, the currents and the upwelling phenomenon,
taken with the ecological importance of the marine environment, means that the sea is not a safe place to dump in the long term.
Once these substances are released into, or escape into, the sea they may be absorbed by phytoplankton, move through the food
chains, and collect in the larger organisms, particularly the larger carnivores. When these are caught and eaten or used in fertilisers
on land, the toxins then accumulate in land organisms. All organisms everywhere may be ultimately threatened by dumping.

The economic importance of algae

1. In the laboratory

Agar (also known as agar-agar) is a colloid obtained from various red algae. Agar is only soluble in hot water. A dilute solution of agar (1–2%) remains liquid (sol) down to a temperature of about 35–40°C, after which it will set (change to gel). On reheating, the gel liquifies at about 90°C. Agar is used in the laboratory to solidify culture media for growing bacteria and fungi. It is a non-nitrogenous organic compound, a polysaccharide of galactose residues, and it is not normally digested by the enzymes of micro-organisms.

Until 1939, agar was obtained from Japan where it was extracted from the species of red alga *Gelidium*. From 1939–45 many countries investigated alternative sources. In the UK the algae *Gigartina* spp and *Chondrus crispus* are used. To obtain agar, the seaweed is washed and dried and the gel extracted and filtered. Then the filtrate is frozen and thawed, removing more water with soluble impurities, and the solid agar is flaked and bleached.

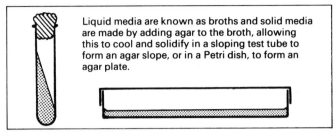

Liquid media are known as broths and solid media are made by adding agar to the broth, allowing this to cool and solidify in a sloping test tube to form an agar slope, or in a Petri dish, to form an agar plate.

2. In the pharmaceutical and food industries

Gels from seaweeds are used in drugs and medicines, for example in tablets to make them soluble in water, and also in foods such as blancmange, 'instant whips', ice-cream, sweets, chocolates, in the baking industry, and also in the packing of meats.

Figure 4.35 Red algae from which agar is extracted

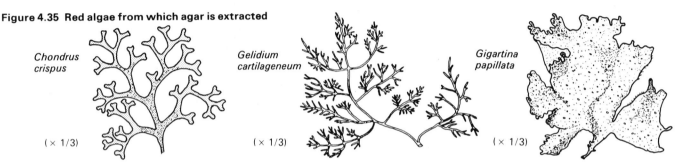

Chondrus crispus (× 1/3)

Gelidium cartilageneum (× 1/3)

Gigartina papillata (× 1/3)

3. In agriculture

Large, brown and red algae are used as fertilisers on farmland close to the sea. When compared with farmyard manure seaweed fronds are rich in potassium ions but rather poor in combined nitrogen and phosphate.
On coastal islands dried seaweeds are fed to livestock (mostly sheep) for most of the year. Dried seaweed is also milled into feeding meal for the livestock.

4. Diatomaceous earth, marketed as diatomite, kieselguhr, and as fullers' earth

Diatoms do not have a long evolutionary history when compared with other unicellular organisms, but during and since the Mesozoic period (the Age of Reptiles and Gymnosperms) there have been diatom populations of such density and for such continuous and prolonged periods that they have formed huge fossil deposits. The thickest deposits are from marine species, but freshwater deposits occur in the beds of former lakes. Such deposits are made up of 86–88% silica, and when a sample is heated strongly to drive off combustible material (organic remains and contaminants) there may be a weight loss of only 4%. These marine deposits known as diatomaceous earth are found in layers many hundreds of feet thick, and are now quarried if they lie inland and above sea-level as a result of geological change.
The major market for diatomaceous earth is in filtration. About 70% of the total production is used in industrial filtration, e.g. sugar refinement, beers, and drugs such as antibiotics produced by cultures of micro-organisms in huge vats. Diatomaceous earth is also used as an inert, mineral filler in paints, plastics and papers, in the insulation of boilers and blast furnaces, and as a mild abrasive in polishes and toothpastes.

Figure 4.36(i) Fullers' earth deposits near Redhill, Surrey. Exposed seams of mineral are dug and quarried. The processing plant is nearby. Farming land and the pattern of fields and hedgerows are at least temporarily disturbed during the extraction process

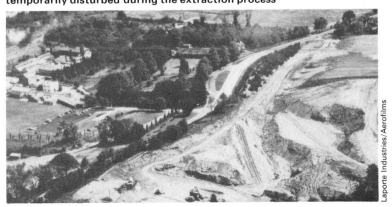

Laporte Industries/Aerofilms

Figure 4.36(ii) The arrangement of geological strata, and the position of fullers' earth, near Redhill

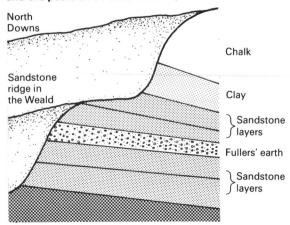

North Downs

Chalk

Sandstone ridge in the Weald

Clay

Sandstone layers

Fullers' earth

Sandstone layers

Algae and pollution

1. In eutrophic lakes and rivers

Eutrophic habitats have a good supply of plant nutrients, potentially a high productivity, and usually support a rich phytoplankton and animal population. Oligotrophic habitats (e.g. tarns and high mountain lakes) are in the opposite condition, low in organic and inorganic nutrients. The process of eutrophication is a normal, long-term enriching and ageing process in natural waters. On the other hand it may be artificial. Man-caused eutrophication can occur at high speed and can have drastic side effects. The causes of sudden eutrophication include:

(a) The application of top-dressings of very soluble artificial fertilisers containing nitrate salts and ions to various cash crops in spring and early summer. Much of this may leach out or run off in heavy rain storms into ponds and streams. These salts are of great value to aquatic plants and this phenomenon may result in a population explosion of plankton and filamentous algae.

(b) The contamination of ponds, streams and rivers with excess detergents from domestic or industrial sources. These mixtures are rich in phosphates which are also of great value to aquatic plants, including algae.

(c) The contamination of streams and rivers with raw (untreated) sewage rich in combined, available nitrogen in urea, amino acids, and so on.

The result is a vast population of algae, known as an 'algal bloom', and this leads to a rapid build-up of organic matter as a result of their photosynthesis. Soon the algae die and their bodies are attacked by bacteria during decay. Thus, the bacterial population now increases and these bacteria use up the dissolved oxygen. Oxygen in the water is very rapidly depleted and animal life, most notably the larger fish, are killed by anaerobic conditions. The water develops a most unpleasant odour. The succession of changes in contaminated water may be followed by observing the changing population of organisms. A small number of organisms are adapted to survive in conditions of low oxygen concentration and are said to be 'indicator species'. Certain species of *Cladophora* are algal indicators of sewage discharge (see Figure 4.5, page 21). When bacteria have reduced the dead organic matter to simple substances, the stream or river returns to normal again.

Figure 4.37 The effects of pollution of a river with untreated sewage, and the subsequent recovery stages

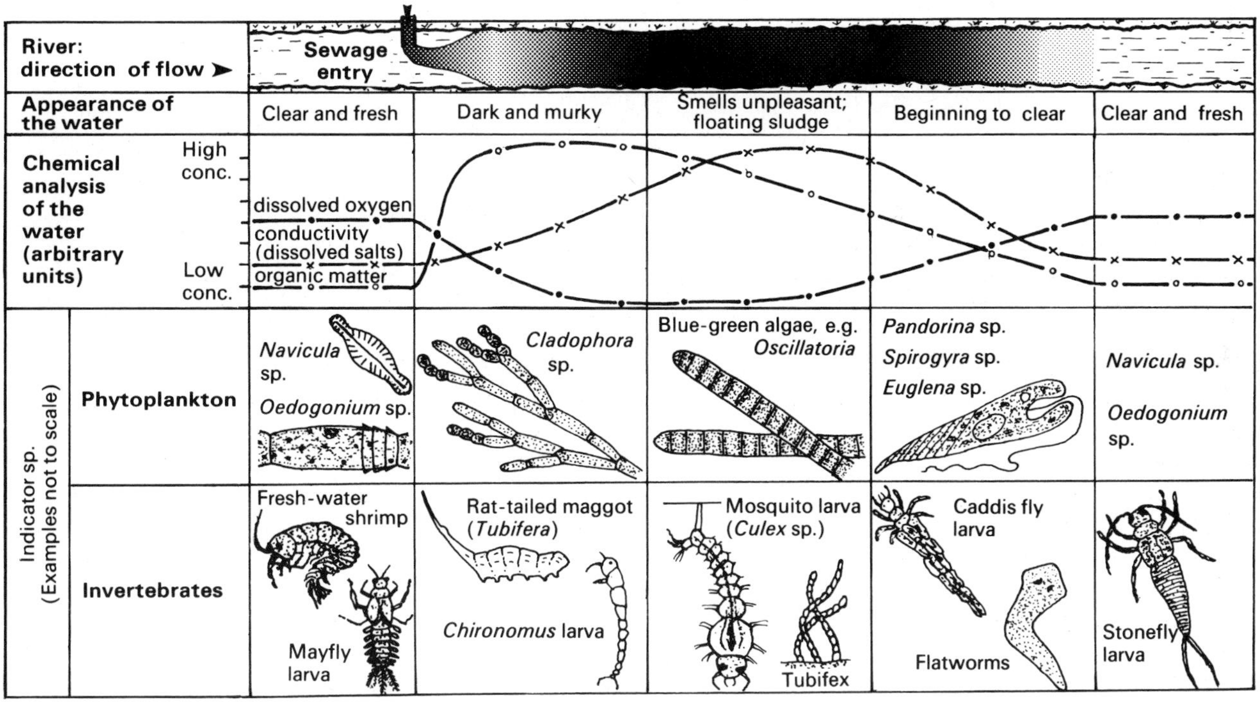

River: direction of flow ➤		Sewage entry				
Appearance of the water		Clear and fresh	Dark and murky	Smells unpleasant; floating sludge	Beginning to clear	Clear and fresh
Chemical analysis of the water (arbitrary units)	High conc. / Low conc.	dissolved oxygen / conductivity (dissolved salts) / organic matter				
Indicator sp. (Examples not to scale) — Phytoplankton		*Navicula* sp. / *Oedogonium* sp.	*Cladophora* sp.	Blue-green algae, e.g. *Oscillatoria*	*Pandorina* sp. / *Spirogyra* sp. / *Euglena* sp.	*Navicula* sp. / *Oedogonium* sp.
Indicator sp. (Examples not to scale) — Invertebrates		Fresh-water shrimp / Mayfly larva	Rat-tailed maggot (*Tubifera*) / *Chironomus* larva	Mosquito larva (*Culex* sp.) / Tubifex	Caddis fly larva / Flatworms	Stonefly larva

2. By Japanese Seaweed (Japweed, *Sargassum muticulum*)

This is a Brown seaweed, native to Japan, which was introduced into British Columbia in the 1940s and has since extended southwards into California. It was possibly introduced into European waters in ballast water, on the bottom of ships or as packaging around oysters. It was first found in Britain around the Isle of Wight in 1973 and since then has spread along the south coast. Marine biologists fear that it may be as successful here as it is on the western seaboard of North America and displace our indigenous Brown algae, expecially *Laminaria* and the marine angiosperm *Zostera marina* (Eel-Grass). There is evidence that these changes may also support much reduced populations of other organisms. *Sargassum muticulum* may affect local recreational amenities by fouling fishing lines, nets and the propellers of small boats. Fouling of marinas and an increase in cast-up and drifting Japweed on shores is also a possibility. Various groups and official bodies have attempted to clear *Sargassum muticulum* from Britain, but this has not been successful.

Figure 4.38 Japanese Seaweed (Japweed, *Sargassum muticulum*)

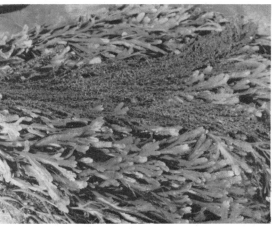

Dr W. Farnham

Fungi

Fungi comprise the moulds, yeasts, mildews, mushrooms, puffballs and rusts. They are organisms that feed on organic matter, generally as saprophytes, sometimes as parasites; they lack chlorophyll. The fungal body (the mycelium) is filamentous and made of fine, colourless branching threads (hyphae). Each hypha is surrounded by a wall and the cytoplasm contains nuclei and organelles. Remember that we are now dealing with eukaryotes (see page 4) which have a nucleus separated from the cytoplasm by a nuclear membrane, and the cytoplasm contains membranous organelles such as mitochondria. The study of fungi is called mycology. The fungi are now considered to be members of a separate kingdom, different from plants and animals.

Spores and hyphae

Fungi exist as the hyphae of a mycelium. At some stage, spores are produced on a specialised part of the mycelium. The spores are dormant structures, many are short-lived. They have little protection against desiccation, ultra-violet (UV) light or predators. Vast numbers of spores are produced and dispersed. If they do not land in favourable conditions and are not destroyed they remain dormant. In a favourable environment a spore quickly swells, a germ tube grows out, and the hypha elongates rapidly and soon branches. This process is called germination.

Figure 5.1 Stages in the germination of a fungal spore

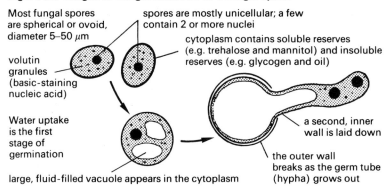

Most fungal spores are spherical or ovoid, diameter 5–50 μm

spores are mostly unicellular; a few contain 2 or more nuclei

cytoplasm contains soluble reserves (e.g. trehalose and mannitol) and insoluble reserves (e.g. glycogen and oil)

volutin granules (basic-staining nucleic acid)

Water uptake is the first stage of germination

a second, inner wall is laid down

the outer wall breaks as the germ tube (hypha) grows out

large, fluid-filled vacuole appears in the cytoplasm

An interpretation of the electron micrograph

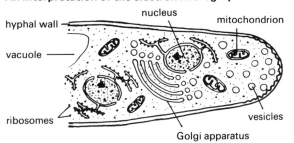

hyphal wall · nucleus · mitochondrion · vacuole · ribosomes · vesicles · Golgi apparatus

Figure 5.2 Electron micrograph of germinated sporangiophore

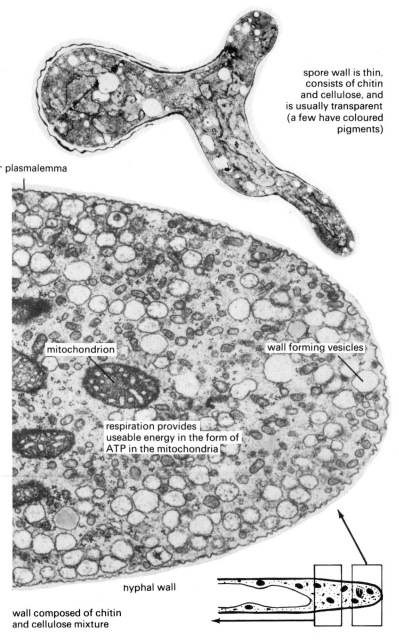

spore wall is thin, consists of chitin and cellulose, and is usually transparent (a few have coloured pigments)

plasmalemma

mitochondrion

respiration provides useable energy in the form of ATP in the mitochondria

wall forming vesicles

hyphal wall

wall composed of chitin and cellulose mixture

Figure 5.3 The structure of the hypha

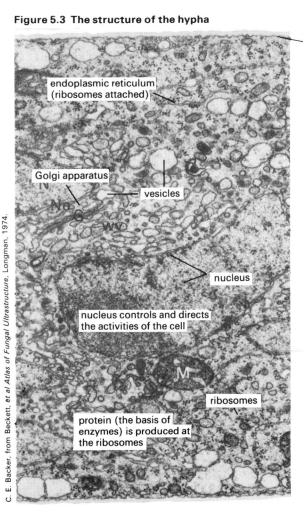

endoplasmic reticulum (ribosomes attached)

Golgi apparatus

vesicles

nucleus

nucleus controls and directs the activities of the cell

ribosomes

protein (the basis of enzymes) is produced at the ribosomes

C. E. Backer, from Beckett, et al Atlas of Fungal Ultrastructure, Longman, 1974.

Growth of hyphae

Growth of hyphae is quick under favourable conditions. Each hypha both grows at its tip and divides repeatedly along its length, locating and trapping new food supplies. Waste products are left behind, either in the older hyphae, or in the substrate. The shape of the colony formed in this way depends on external conditions. On laboratory agar plates we may observe circular colonies; in nature, growth is not necessarily equally rewarded in every direction. The absence of food, the accumulation of harmful substances, or the actions of predators or competitors may retard growth locally. The main hyphal-axis grows fastest, lateral branches grow more slowly, and the older branches may stop altogether. Cross-walls are formed in some species. In coenocytic hyphae (i.e. no cross-walls, not divided into cells see *Mucor* and *Rhizopus*, page 42) few later-formed cross-walls are found. In cellular fungi (see *Neurospora*, page 51 and *Agaricus*, page 54) there are numerous cross-walls with perforations or pores in them.

Figure 5.5 One day's growth of a fungal colony from a single spore (malt agar plate). Part of the colony is shown enlarged and alternately shaded to show extensions at 10 minute intervals over one hour of growth

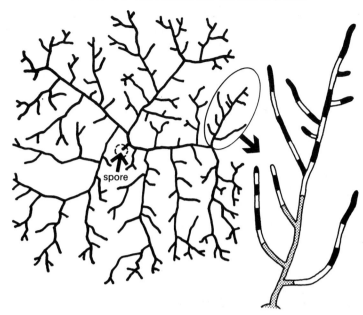

Adapted from data given in Ingold, C. T. *The Biology of Fungi.* Hutchinson, 1952

Protoplasmic streaming occurs within the hyphae, and results in the transport of cytoplasm, water and food materials about the organism.

Figure 5.4 Part of a coenocytic mycelium at high magnification (cytoplasmic streaming occurs in the hyphae)

Static cytoplasm lining the inside of the hyphal wall

mass of granular cytoplasm

vacuole

The ingredients of a fungal 'balanced diet'

For successful growth the fungus requires nutrients and favourable conditions

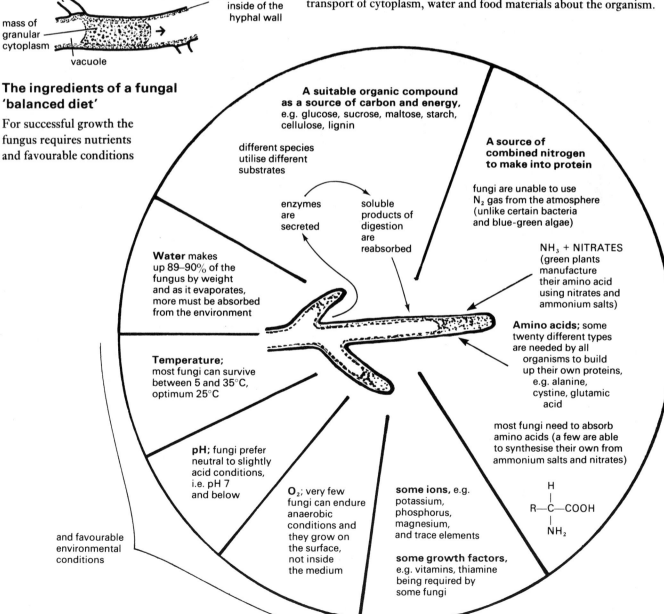

A suitable organic compound as a source of carbon and energy, e.g. glucose, sucrose, maltose, starch, cellulose, lignin

different species utilise different substrates

enzymes are secreted

soluble products of digestion are reabsorbed

A source of combined nitrogen to make into protein

fungi are unable to use N_2 gas from the atmosphere (unlike certain bacteria and blue-green algae)

NH_3 + NITRATES (green plants manufacture their amino acid using nitrates and ammonium salts)

Amino acids; some twenty different types are needed by all organisms to build up their own proteins, e.g. alanine, cystine, glutamic acid

most fungi need to absorb amino acids (a few are able to synthesise their own from ammonium salts and nitrates)

Water makes up 89–90% of the fungus by weight and as it evaporates, more must be absorbed from the environment

Temperature; most fungi can survive between 5 and 35°C, optimum 25°C

pH; fungi prefer neutral to slightly acid conditions, i.e. pH 7 and below

and favourable environmental conditions

O_2; very few fungi can endure anaerobic conditions and they grow on the surface, not inside the medium

some ions, e.g. potassium, phosphorus, magnesium, and trace elements

some growth factors, e.g. vitamins, thiamine being required by some fungi

$$R-\underset{\underset{NH_2}{|}}{\overset{\overset{H}{|}}{C}}-COOH$$

The range of fungi

1. The plant-like fungi (Phycomycetes)

This is a collection of over 1700 different species all at approximately the same level of organisation and complexity. It is not a 'natural' group of closely related organisms. The fungal body (mycelium) is usually of branched coenocytic hyphae. The spore-producing structures are not grouped into a complex fruit body. This group includes microscopic aquatic fungi, water moulds and downy mildews, and the pin moulds. For examples look at *Mucor* and *Rhizopus* (pages 42–43), *Phytophthora* (page 62) and the parasitic mould fungus below.

Figure 5.6 *Peronospora parasitica* **on the stem of a member of the Cruciferae (×100) with interpretive drawing**

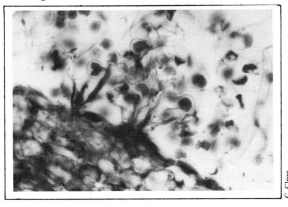

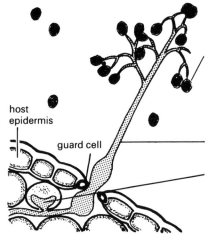

conidia are asexual spores formed at the tips of branching hyphae by rounding off and constriction of the tip of the hyphae

host epidermis

guard cell

the conidiophore is a specialised aerial hypha which produces conidia

hypha of *Peronospora* sp. between the host cells: hyphae penetrate individual cells and swell-up into a large organ (haustonium) which digests the cell contents and absorbs the products of digestion

2. The sac fungi (Ascomycetes)

This is the largest group within the fungi, consisting of 15 000 species (30 000 species when all the members existing in Lichens are included (see page 62)). The members of this varied group all produce spores within a sac, called the ascus (pl. *asci*). At maturity the ascus usually contains eight ascospores. In most species the ascus is an explosive sporangium that breaks open and squirts the spores some distance into the air. Ascospores are dispersed by air currents. The ascus and spores develop in a particular way.

Figure 5.7 Stages in the formation of ascospores in an ascus

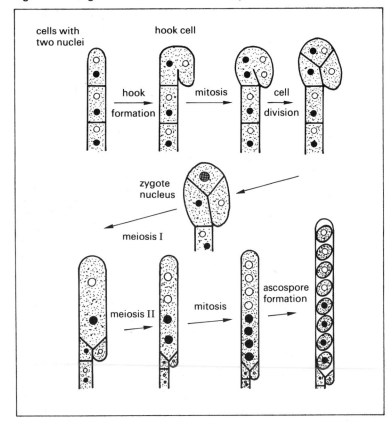

cells with two nuclei

hook cell

hook formation → mitosis → cell division

zygote nucleus

meiosis I

meiosis II → mitosis → ascospore formation

Figure 5.8 The mycelium as a three-dimensional network

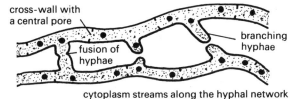

cross-wall with a central pore

fusion of hyphae

branching hyphae

cytoplasm streams along the hyphal network

Figure 5.9 A cylindrical ascus containing eight ascospores, as observed just prior to explosive discharge (×250)

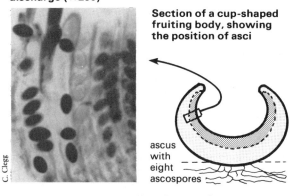

Section of a cup-shaped fruiting body, showing the position of asci

ascus with eight ascospores

Figure 5.10 The Orange Peel Fungus. A spore-producing layer (asci packed with sterile hyphae) develops within a shallow cup

In most species there is a complex fruiting body in which the asci are grouped (not the case in yeasts). The mycelium is branched and septate, with one to several nuclei per cell. The cross-walls are perforated with a minute central pore, permitting cytoplasmic streaming. Fusion of hyphae frequently occurs between neighbouring branches so that the mycelium is a three-dimensional network.

3. The club fungi (Basidiomycetes)

This is the second largest group within the fungi, consisting of about 11 000 species. It includes the largest species – mushrooms, bracket fungi, puff-balls and stink-horns – and also some relatively inconspicuous members such as the parasitic rusts and smuts, which parasitise cereal crops and reduce their yield. Club fungi produce spores, usually four, on the surface of a club-shaped sporangium called a basidium (pl. basidia).

Figure 5.11 Formation of a basidium with basidiospores

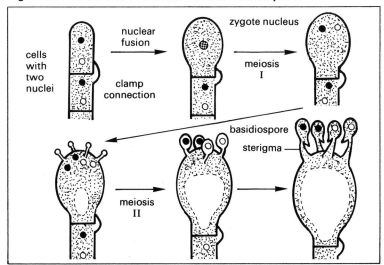

Figure 5.12 The septum between hyphal cells

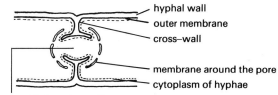

pore (dolipore) permits
movement of cytoplasm along hyphae

Within the mycelium fusion of hypha converts the whole into a three-dimensional network, as in the sac fungi. The cells are usually binucleate, and many species have clamp connections at the cross-walls.

Figure 5.13 Clamp-connections between cells

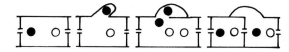

In most species there is a complex fruiting body on which the basidia are packed. The mycelium consists of branched, septate hyphae with perforated cross-walls.

For examples look at the illustrations of mushrooms (pages 54–61), the rust fungus (page 61), and the Parasol Mushroom below.

Figure 5.14 The Parasol Mushroom (*Lepiota procera*)

Dr A. Beaumont

4. Slime moulds (Myxomycetes)

Slime moulds live in cool, shady, moist places in woods. They can be found on decaying logs, dead leaves, and other organic matter where there is abundant moisture. They are mostly very small organisms. They consist of a blob of protoplasm surrounded by a thin plasma membrane, and in this form they stream over surfaces and feed on bacteria, protozoa and fungal spores.

The spore-producing structures (sporangia) can be very colourful. Each has a skin (peridium) and contains spores held in place by a system of threads (the capillitium). Some species are commonly found on the bark of living trees. Pieces cut from the fissures of rough bark and cultured in a warm, moist chamber often yield one or more species of slime mould.

Figure 5.16 Scanning electron micrograph of sporangium of the slime mould *Macbrideola synsporus* (×12)

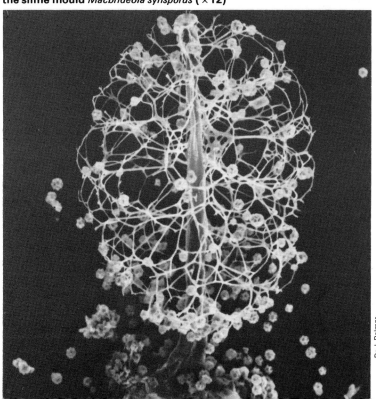

Dr J. Palmer

Figure 5.15 The life-cycle of a slime-mould

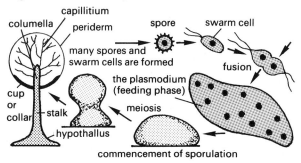

Pin moulds; *Mucor* and *Rhizopus* species

Pin moulds are saprophytic. *Mucor* species commonly occur in the soil or appear on the dung of herbivorous animals (see coprophilous fungi, page 44). *Rhizopus* species are moulds frequently found on damp bread. The hyphae of both types absorb sugars, amino acids and fatty acids, and also secrete enzymes that hydrolyse starch, proteins and fats in the surrounding medium.

Figure 5.17 The branched feeding mycelium of *Mucor* sp. and *Rhizopus* sp.

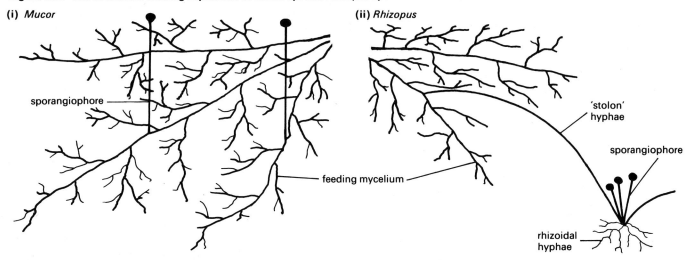

(i) *Mucor*   **(ii)** *Rhizopus*

sporangiophore — feeding mycelium — 'stolon' hyphae — sporangiophore — rhizoidal hyphae

Spore production and dispersal: asexual reproduction by moulds

Provided the environment remains humid and moist, a mould colony produces spores within a few days of becoming established. From within a sporangium, spores (sporangiospores) are produced and dispersed by the air, by insects or by water droplets. Sporangia are formed at the tips of aerial hyphae (sporangiophores) which grow out of feeding mycelium.

Figure 5.18 Stages in sporangiophore growth during the formation of spores. The whole process lasts about one day

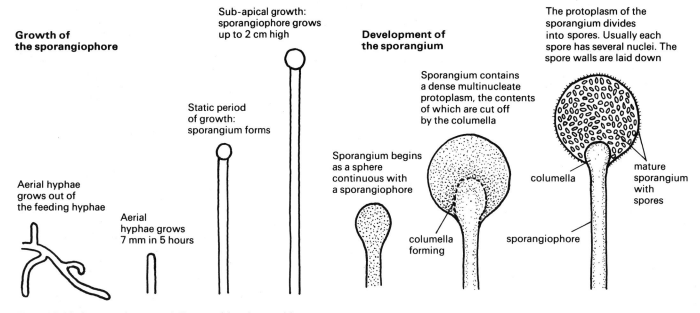

Growth of the sporangiophore

Sub-apical growth: sporangiophore grows up to 2 cm high

Static period of growth: sporangium forms

Aerial hyphae grows out of the feeding hyphae

Aerial hyphae grows 7 mm in 5 hours

Development of the sporangium

Sporangium contains a dense multinucleate protoplasm, the contents of which are cut off by the columella

Sporangium begins as a sphere continuous with a sporangiophore

columella forming

The protoplasm of the sporangium divides into spores. Usually each spore has several nuclei. The spore walls are laid down

columella

sporangiophore

mature sporangium with spores

Figure 5.19 Spore release and dispersal in pin moulds

In *Rhizopus* spp the sporangium wall cracks into many fragments, and the spores inside are a dry, powdery mass. The columella collapses, and spores are blown away.

(*Mucor plumbeus* also shows dry spore dispersal, as in *Rhizopus*.)

dry spores exposed

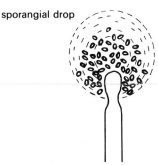

In most species of *Mucor* the sporangium wall dissolves and water passes into the spore mass. If a fly walks over this, or if a rain drop hits it, the spores are dispersed. In dry air the liquid dries and the spores are all cemented to the columella. They are not blown away.

sporangial drop

Spores in the air

When fungal spores in the air are sampled and grown, for every 1000 spores trapped only about 0.2% are pin mould spores, and almost all of these are *Rhizopus* spores. *Mucor* spores are rarely found in the air. This observation can be correlated with their dispersal mechanism. (Most air-borne fungal spores belong to 'sac-fungi' species such as *Penicillium*.)

Figure 5.20 Sporangia of *Rhizopus* sp. showing entire sporangia and some where the columella has collapsed and the spores have been dispersed

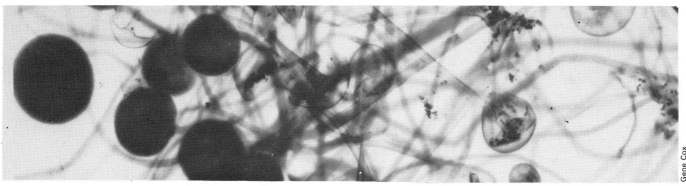

Sexual reproduction in *Mucor*

Sexual reproduction in *Mucor* can be shown in laboratory cultures, but is rare event in nature. Most moulds are heterothallic, that is mycelia of two different strains, designated + and −, must be present. This has the effect of achieving outbreeding. Some species are homothallic, that is zygospores are formed in cultures grown from a single spore.

Figure 5.21 Sexual reproduction in *Rhizopus sexualis* (homothallic species)

Figure 5.22 Sexual reproduction in *Mucor hiemalis* (heterothallic species) as observed in the laboratory

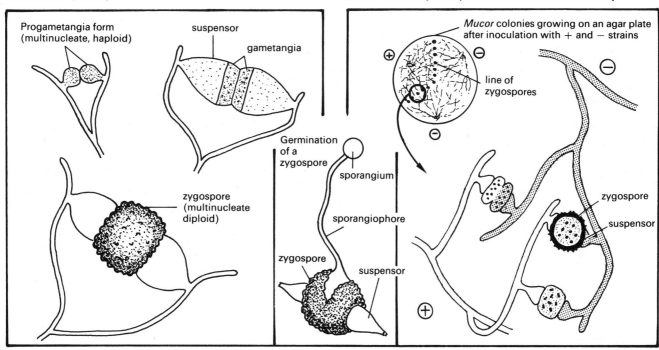

Figure 5.23 Sexual reproduction in *Rhizopus* sp. (×200)

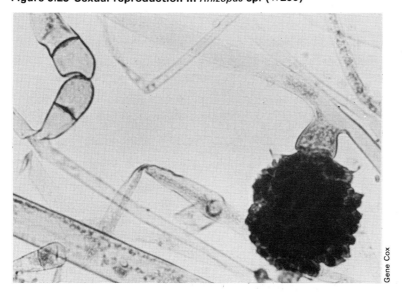

Summary of the life-cycle of *Mucor*

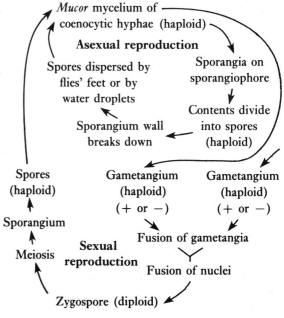

Mucor mycelium of coenocytic hyphae (haploid)

Asexual reproduction

Sporangia on sporangiophore

Contents divide into spores (haploid)

Sporangium wall breaks down

Spores dispersed by flies' feet or by water droplets

Spores (haploid)

Sporangium

Meiosis

Zygospore (diploid)

Sexual reproduction

Fusion of nuclei

Fusion of gametangia

Gametangium (haploid) (+ or −)

Gametangium (haploid) (+ or −)

Coprophilous fungi

The dung of herbivores such as rabbits, horses and cows has a large, natural fungal flora, and when fresh dung is incubated in moist conditions a succession of fungal fruiting bodies always appears. The fruiting bodies are often light-sensitive and orientate so that spores are dispersed towards the light, often by a violent or explosive discharge mechanism. These fungi grow on an irregular surface and phototropism helps to ensure that spore discharge occurs towards an open space. Successful dispersal in coprophilous fungi requires that spores reach the surrounding vegetation. The spore projectile often consists of many spores, the spore walls or sporangial walls are often darkly pigmented (this protects the protoplasm from sunlight) and the whole projectile is often mucilaginous and adheres to any surface it strikes. This surface will often be a green leaf which may eventually be eaten by a herbivore. The spores can withstand passage through the alimentary canal, and many spores actually require such treatment before they can germinate. In the succession of coprophilous fungi that appear on fresh moist dung the majority are present in the dung as spores when it is deposited.

Figure 5.24 A typical succession of fruiting bodies of coprophilous fungi found on herbivorous dung
The spores, with bacteria, are present in the dung when it is deposited.

The first fruiting bodies to appear on the surface of the dung are members of the plant-like and conjugation fungi (see Phycomycetes page 40). They appear in one to seven days and last for up to fourteen days. Examples include, *Mucor* sp., *Pilaria* sp. and *Pilobulus* sp.	Subsequently, fruiting bodies of sac fungi (see Ascomycetes page 40) appear. This occurs after five to six days and they may persist for four to six weeks. Examples include *Ascobolus* sp. and *Sordaria* sp.	Finally, the fruiting bodies of the club-fungi (see Basidiomycetes page 41) appear. This normally occurs after one or two weeks and they persist until the spores have been dispersed. An example is *Coprinus* sp.

Mucor sp. (×200)

Pilaria sp. (×50)

Pilobolus sp. (×50)

sporangium

Ascobolus sp. (×100)

ascospores

Coprinus sp. (Life size)

pileus

spores

Sordaria sp. (×70)

asci

stipe

sporangiophore

sporangiophore

fruiting body

flask-shaped fruiting body

feeding mycelium

dung

Mucor sp., *Pilaria* sp., *Pilobolus* sp..

These fungi absorb any remaining sugars and amino acids and digest starch, fats and proteins in the dung. These relatively short-lived food sources must be exploited quickly by rapid hyphal growth, or they are lost to bacteria

Ascobolus sp., *Sordaria* sp..

These fungi feed by digesting the cellulose and hemicelluloses in the dung, and absorbing the products of digestion back into the mycelium

Coprinus sp..

These fungi feed by digesting the lignified (woody) remains of fibres and xylems vessels in the dung

Figure 5.25 *Pilobolus kleinii* **sporangiophores on horse dung (×5)**

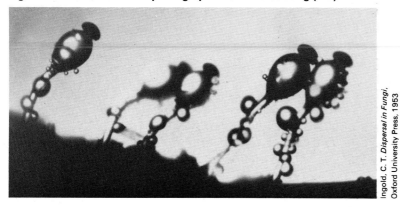

Ingold, C. T. *Dispersal in Fungi*, Oxford University Press, 1953

Apparatus used for incubation of herbivorous dung

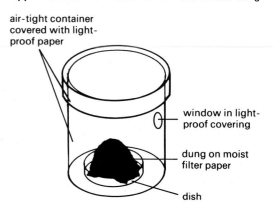

air-tight container covered with light-proof paper

window in light-proof covering

dung on moist filter paper

dish

Figure 5.26 Sporangium dispersal in *Pilobolus*

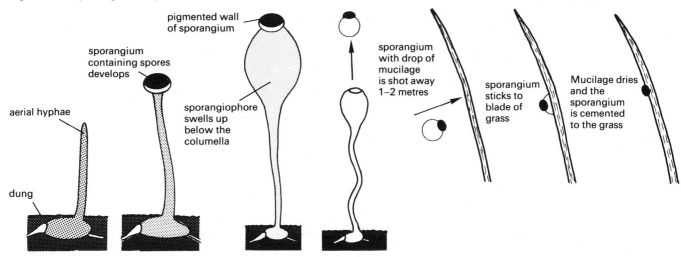

pigmented wall of sporangium

sporangium containing spores develops

aerial hyphae

sporangiophore swells up below the columella

dung

sporangium with drop of mucilage is shot away 1–2 metres

sporangium sticks to blade of grass

Mucilage dries and the sporangium is cemented to the grass

Figure 5.27 Spore dispersal in *Sordaria* and photomicrograph of asci container

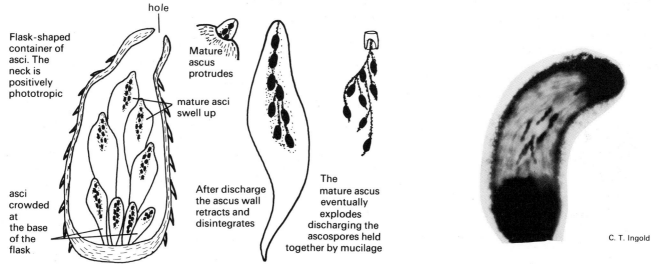

hole

Flask-shaped container of asci. The neck is positively phototropic

Mature ascus protrudes

mature asci swell up

asci crowded at the base of the flask

After discharge the ascus wall retracts and disintegrates

The mature ascus eventually explodes discharging the ascospores held together by mucilage

C. T. Ingold

Garden compost

In nature, soil fertility is maintained by decomposition of dead plants and animals and also their products, at or near the soil surface. This is a slow process. In the garden compost heap the process can be speeded up by maintaining a large compact heap of moist vegetable matter within an insulated box (e.g. one made from straw bales) protected from excess rain. The heap must be well aerated. Aerobic breakdown generates heat and the conservation of heat speeds the decay and helps kill weeds, seeds and disease organisms. The well rotted compost can then be dug into the soil. Further slow decay of this humus makes available to plants their nutritional requirements.

The heating of the compost heap is due to the very active metabolism of many micro-organisms within closely-packed, chopped vegetable matter which is supplied with sufficient water and combined nitrogen for growth and metabolism. The temperature rises to 60–70°C in a period of one to several weeks (depending on the season). In the absence of air anaerobic decay (putrifaction) generates an unpleasant smell and permits only slow, partial decay with little heat generated.

There is a sequence of micro-organism involved in aerobic decay within compost:

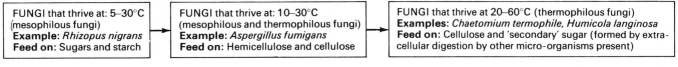

| FUNGI that thrive at: 5–30°C (mesophilous fungi) **Example:** *Rhizopus nigrans* **Feed on:** Sugars and starch | FUNGI that thrive at: 10–30°C (mesophilous and thermophilous fungi) **Example:** *Aspergillus fumigans* **Feed on:** Hemicellulose and cellulose | FUNGI that thrive at 20–60°C (thermophilous fungi) **Examples:** *Chaetomium termophile, Humicola langinosa* **Feed on:** Cellulose and 'secondary' sugar (formed by extra-cellular digestion by other micro-organisms present) |

Figure 5.28 A compost heap, and the variation of temperature within it

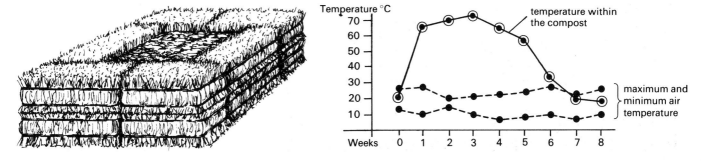

Temperature °C

temperature within the compost

maximum and minimum air temperature

Weeks   0   1   2   3   4   5   6   7   8

Yeasts

Yeasts are unicellular fungi that bud profusely under favourable conditions (Figure 5.30, below). They are classified as sac-fungi (Ascomycetes) even though they are unicellular. Yeasts are common where sugar occurs; their name saccharomyces means 'sugar fungi'. They grown on the surface of fruits, in the nectar of flowers, in sap exuded from trees, in the soil and in freshwater. Yeasts are of great economic importance (see pages 48–49) and are frequently exploited in biochemical research, e.g. concerning enzymes and respiration.

Figure 5.29 Drawing from an electron micrograph of a thin- section of a yeast cell

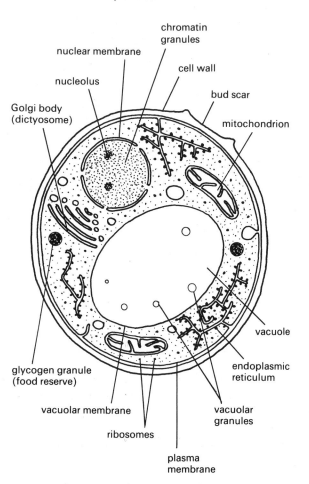

- chromatin granules
- nuclear membrane
- nucleolus
- cell wall
- bud scar
- Golgi body (dictyosome)
- mitochondrion
- glycogen granule (food reserve)
- vacuole
- endoplasmic reticulum
- vacuolar membrane
- vacuolar granules
- ribosomes
- plasma membrane

Figure 5.30 Life-cycle of baker's yeast: *Saccharomyces cervisiae*

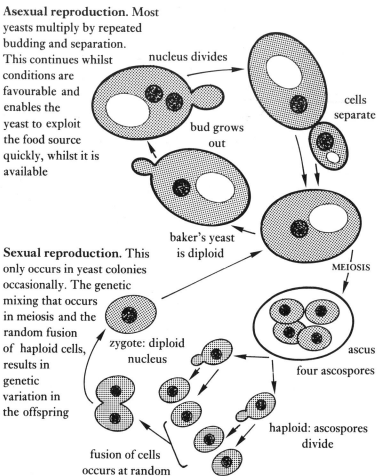

Asexual reproduction. Most yeasts multiply by repeated budding and separation. This continues whilst conditions are favourable and enables the yeast to exploit the food source quickly, whilst it is available

nucleus divides

bud grows out

cells separate

baker's yeast is diploid

MEIOSIS

ascus

four ascospores

haploid: ascospores divide

Sexual reproduction. This only occurs in yeast colonies occasionally. The genetic mixing that occurs in meiosis and the random fusion of haploid cells, results in genetic variation in the offspring

zygote: diploid nucleus

fusion of cells occurs at random

Figure 5.31 Scanning electron micrograph of brewer's yeast (*Saccharomyces cerevisiae*) **budding** (× 10 000)

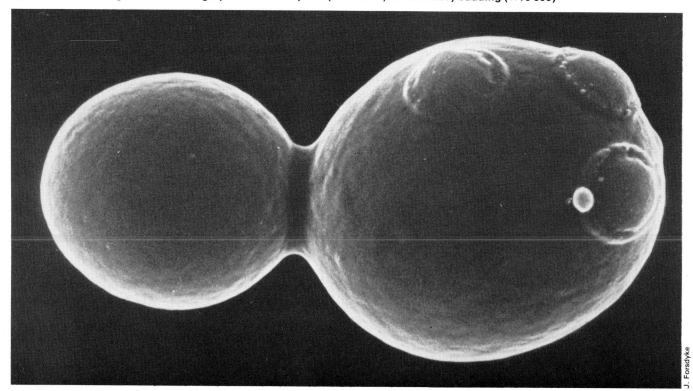

J. Forsdyke

Figure 5.32 Scanning electron micrograph of yeast cells from liquid culture (× 2 000). Daughter cells themselves may produce buds before separation from parent cells has occurred. Successive budding results in a chain of cells referred to as a pseudomycelium

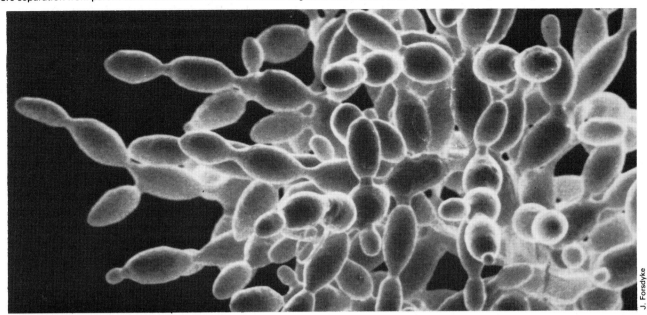

Respiration

Many species of yeast respire anaerobically, producing alcohol, carbon dioxide and a little energy.

$$C_6H_{12}O_6 \longrightarrow 2C_2H_5OH + 2CO_2 + \text{ENERGY}$$

Some species of yeast respire aerobically if oxygen is available, producing carbon dioxide, water and much energy.

$$C_6H_{12}O_6 + 6O_2 \longrightarrow 6CO_2 + 6H_2O + \text{ENERGY}$$

The details of the chemical steps (the biochemical pathway) of respiration have been worked out in yeast and other organisms by:

(a) extracting and isolating all the postulated intermediates from cells;

(b) isolating the enzymes that can catalyse each step or reaction in the cell (*in vivo*) and outside the cell (*in vitro*);

(c) interruption of the pathway of respiration in intact cells by applying specific inhibitors (chemicals that impare the action of an enzyme) or fixatives (chemicals that react with an intermediate and isolate it from further change) which block the sequence at predicted points and cause an intermediate to accumulate;

(d) 'feeding experiments' – the application of radioactively labelled intermediates to intact cells and the detection of radioactive carbon dioxide and other products.

A summary of the pathway of fermentation in yeast in the absence of air — glycolysis

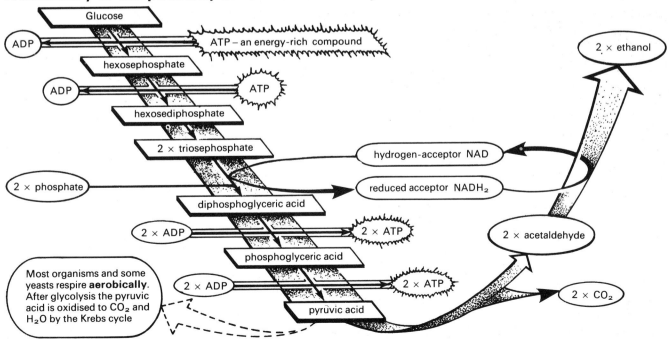

Respiration occurs in every living cell. Tissue respiration is the biochemical change illustrated above. Gaseous exchange occurs between the cell and the environment. In small organisms the surface area is sufficient for this to occur by diffusion over the whole body surface, and in these organisms there are no organs of gaseous exchange.

Yeast in the food and drink industry

1. Alcoholic drinks

(a) **Beer production.** The brewing of beer has been going on for thousands of years, using not only barley but also maize and millet in Africa, and rice in Asia. Today beer is brewed from 'malting barley' that is high in starch content and in the hydrolysing enzymes (mostly diastase). The grains must be free from fungus infections. The first stage in brewing is the germination of barley under controlled conditions in order to convert food reserves in the grain to sugar, amino acids and fatty acids by the action of enzymes from the barley grains. (Yeast does not produce enzymes that can catalyse these changes.)

The steps in beer production are as follows:

> **Malting**
> Barley grains are soaked for 2–3 days, drained, and incubated for 10 days at 13–17°C. Roots and shoots start to grow. Starch reserves are mobilised as sugar. The temperature is then raised to between 40 and 70°C to halt germination.

> **Cracking**
> Grains are heated to 80°C for a light roasting before they are passed between rollers which crack them open.

> **Mashing**
> With hot water at 62–68°C the sugars and amino acids are washed from the grains. Left behind from this process are brewer's grains, used in the feeding of milking herds of cows. These brewer's grains arrive at the farm in lorry-loads and are stored in cool, concrete chambers, pressed down to exclude air and thus reduce decay and deterioration.

> **Boiling**
> The liquor from the mashing process, known as wort, is boiled for several hours to concentrate it. Dried hops are added for flavour and for their anti-microbial properties. Cooling follows.

> **Fermentation**
> Yeast is now added, *Saccharomyces cerevisiae* or *S. carlsbergensis*, which converts sugar to ethanol and carbon dioxide over a period of 2–5 days. As the yeast grows it forms a thick head which is skimmed off the surface. This is sold as a cake or as a slurry (see yeast extract below). The carbon dioxide produced is solidified at low temperature and under high pressure and sold as dry ice.

> **Conditioning**
> The beer should be 4–8% ethanol (10% in barley wine). It is stored in barrels to allow final fermentation and for clearing of the yeast.
> Under modern quality control and marketing procedures it may be filtered, pasteurised, standardised (brought to a consistent colour and flavour), and canned.

(b) **Wine production.** Wine is produced from ripe grapes. For white wine only the juice and pulp is used, but for red wine the skins and pips are also included. The juice is fermented by yeasts that occur naturally on the grapes. Sugar is turned to alcohol, and when the concentration reaches 15% it kills the yeasts. The wine is matured in casks and then filtered before bottling.

2. Bread-making

Bread is produced from wheat flour.

Hard wheats contain more protein and make better bread. They come from areas of limited rainfall, e.g. parts of USA, Canada and USSR.
Soft wheats are more starchy, and are made into pastries, pastas and into bread which is to be consumed quickly. They are grown in the more humid general-farming areas, e.g. in Europe.

The steps in bread production are as follows:

> **Flour milling**
> The grains are passed between rollers and become bran (flattened embryos) and flour (powdered endosperm). Commercial flour is marketed either as **wholemeal flour** containing 95% of the grain with only the coarse bran removed; or as **white flour** containing 70% of the grain with bran and much of the embryos removed. At this stage vitamins, bleaching agents and 'improvers' may be added.

> **Dough mixed**
> The flour is mixed with fat, salt and water. Flour enzymes convert some starch to sugar. Protein fibres are stretched to a fine, silky structure.

> **Bulk fermentation**
> Baker's yeast is added, and in the warm dough sugar is fermented to carbon dioxide and ethanol, giving the dough a light, porous structure.

> **Dividing, moulding, proving and baking**
> The risen dough is stretched and kneaded, the protein fibres being further stretched by the developing gas bubbles (carbon dioxide) as well as by this mechanical mixing. The loaf is then baked.

Modern practice in bread-making involves many additions, including sugar for fermentation, and many chemicals as bleaching agents and 'improving' agents. Over the past few years there has been some concern about the desirability of adding these chemicals to bread. Some time ago a newspaper carried an article with the headline 'Should bread carry a Government Health Warning?' The article referred to white bread, not wholemeal bread. The cereal fibres found in wholemeal bread may protect us against digestive disorders. Wholemeal flour contains more vitamins, protein and iron than white flour. White flour contains additives such as acetone peroxide, azodicarbonamide and chlorine dioxide. These chemicals, or others, are added to remove naturally-occurring harmless colouring, and to reduce the activity of natural enzymes in flour. The additives are believed to be harmless.

3. Yeast Extract

Large quantities of fresh yeast are available as a waste product of brewing. Much of this is used in the preparation of yeast extract.

> **Yeast from the brewery**
> 80% of yeast from each brew is redundant (20% is re-used in brewing).

> **Autolysis**
> Autolysis (self-digestion by enzymes in aged and dying cells) occurs in the yeast cake or slurry in transit from the brewery.

> **Heat treatment**
> The cells are killed by raising the temperature just high enough to destroy the cell membranes but not high enough to inactivate the hydrolytic enzymes. Self-digestion continues, e.g. proteins are converted to amino acids.

> **Centrifugation**
> A precipitate of cell walls and protein slime is separated, dried and used in the manufacture of animal feeding stuff. The remaining supernatant liquid contains 5–8% solids. This is concentrated by evaporation to the point where the extract is 25–50% solid matter.

> **Flavour modification**
> The flavour of the extract is modified by the addition of vegetable extracts. The resulting yeast extract contains vitamins of the B complex. It is sold as 'Marmite' or other proprietary brands of yeast extract, and is used to replace meat extract in cooking, or as a flavoured drink.

Single cell protein (SCP): food from micro-organisms

The industrial micro-biologist may be the farmer of the future! Single cell protein can be derived from bacteria, yeasts and fungi by the fermentation of suitable energy rich substrates, or from algae. The micro-organisms are grown in a suitable medium, then separated from it, dried and sold as cattle food. SCP is 50–80% protein and has a high content of amino-acids (not bound into proteins), vitamins and minerals. It also contains a useable energy store in the form of lipids and carbohydrates.

Animal feeds are currently manufactured from cereal grains, soybean, fishmeal, or oil-seeds. SCP is important as an additional high-quality foodstuff for live-stock.

A suitable substrate for SCP manufacture is methanol from natural gas. ICI uses methanol in the manufacture of 'PRUTEEN' – see Figures 5.33 and 5.34. This process requires costly plant, skilled workers, advanced supply industries and a developed animal feed market. Third world countries require the development of village level technology by which unpalatable waste-products, such as cellulose from farming waste, can be fermented by fungi, dried in the hot sun and the solidified fungal mycelium fed directly to animals.

Figure 5.33 The process of 'PRUTEEN' manufacture from continuous culture of the bacteria *Methylophilus* sp. (ICI)

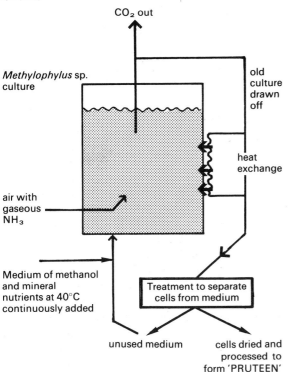

Figure 5.34 ICI Agricultural Division's 'PRUTEEN' plant at Billingham, Cleveland

ICI Agricultural Division

SCP from blue-green algae

The blue-green alga *Spirulina* grows in open ponds. It is photosynthetic, requiring only carbon dioxide, water, light, inorganic salts and ions to live. It grows quickly in warm, salty or alkaline conditions. Dried cultures of this alga are of high food value, and since the cell walls are not made of cellulose it is easily digested by animals. For centuries it has been eaten in the form of dried biscuits or mats in Central Africa and in South America where it grows in alkaline ponds, and is collected, then laid out to dry in the sun. Now industrial production is under way in chemical plants, or in large bodies of warm water from cooling plants. Under optimum conditions the yield from *Spirulina* exceeds that of traditional crops.

Figure 5.35 Scanning electron micrograph of the blue-green alga *Spirulina platensis* (×1 500)

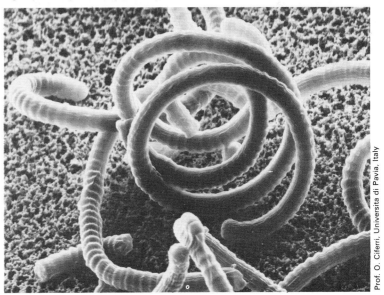

Prof. O. Ciferri, Universita di Pavia, Italy

Yield of traditional crops, and cultures of *Spirulina*

	Yield (tonnes/ha/year)	
	Dry weight	Crude protein
Wheat	4	0.5
Maize	7	1.0
Soya bean	6	2.4
Spirulina	50	35.0

Figure 5.36 The food value of *Spirulina*

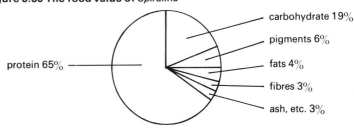

protein 65%
carbohydrate 19%
pigments 6%
fats 4%
fibres 3%
ash, etc. 3%

Aspergillus and Penicillium

These two genera are extremely common fungi; *Aspergillus* in the tropics, *Penicillium* in temperate regions. The majority of air-borne spores are of these two genera. Most species are saprophytic, they colonise damp paper, leather and cloth. They occur on decaying organic matter in the soil. The moulds formed may be black, brown, green or blue depending upon specific pigments in the wall of the spores.

Figure 5.37 *Penicillium* **sp. growing on an orange**

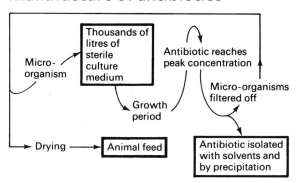

Figure 5.38 Part of *Aspergillus* **mycelium showing the cell structure and feeding mechanism**

hyphae consist of branched, multinucleate cells

nucleus

cytoplasm

cell wall

Mycelium produces a variety of enzymes, depending on the substrate on which it grows

Products of digestion are absorbed back into the cells

The presence of a particular substrate induces synthesis of the enzymes to hydrolyse it, e.g. for starch, cellulose and proteins

Chains of asexual spores (conidia, i.e. formed on the tips of hyphae, not within a sporangium) are produced from projections (phialides) on special hyphae (conidiophores). In *Aspergillus* spp the conidiophores are characteristically terminated in a bulbous head (mop head); in *Penicillium* spp the conidiophores are much branched (brush head).

Figure 5.39 Conidia production in *Penicillium* **sp. (× 700)**

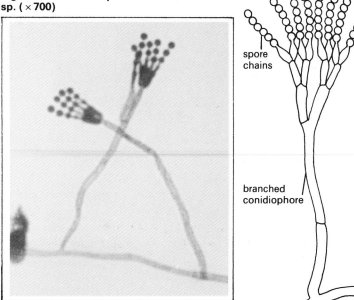

spore chains

branched conidiophore

Penicillin and other antibiotics

The production of antibiotics by micro-organisms is an example of chemical warfare in nature. Alexander Fleming (1891–1955) first reported this action in 1929 when he noticed that the growth of *Staphylococcus aureus* on an agar plate, was suppressed, and the bacteria eventually destroyed, in the presence of the fungus *Penicillium notatum*. Penicillin was developed from this fungus in the early 1940s and it has since been found that it works against certain bacteria by interfering with the biochemistry of cell wall formation during growth. Today mutant strains of the fungus grown from *Penicillium chrysogenum*, that has been irradiated with UV-light, produce enormously increased yields of penicillin. Penicillin is only effective against a few pathogens all of which are gram-positive bacteria. Since the discovery of penicillin, there has been a systematic search for other bacteria and fungi which produce antibiotics which will, in dilute solution, destroy other micro-organisms. In addition many synthetic antibiotics have been manufactured. Some antibiotics are termed 'broad-spectrum', and are effective against a wide range of organisms. One broad-spectrum antibiotic, called chloramphenicol, originally isolated from *Streptomyces*, is now produced synthetically.

Manufacture of antibiotics

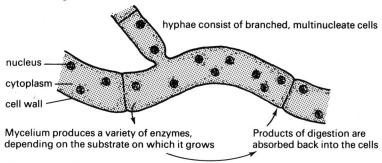

Micro-organism

Thousands of litres of sterile culture medium

Growth period

Antibiotic reaches peak concentration

Micro-organisms filtered off

Drying → Animal feed

Antibiotic isolated with solvents and by precipitation

Figure 5.40 The results of an experiment on the effect of *Penicillium* **fungus on four different species of bacteria, showing the growth of certain species has been inhibited. Three stages are shown on one plate**

Stage one
The plate has been inoculated with *Penicillium* (centre spot) and with four different species of bacteria:
1. *Escherichia coli*
2. *Bacillus subtilis*
3. *Staphylococcus aureus*
4. *Sarcina lutea*

Stage two
The micro-organism have grown and established colonies, having adapted to the food sources available

lysis of bacterial colonies

Stage three

Stage one

Stage two

The growth of colonies 1 and 2 are unaffected

Stage three
The growth of colonies 3 and 4 is inhibited by penicillin that diffuses out from the penicillin mould

Clegg, A. G. and Clegg, P. C. *Man Against Disease*, Heinemann, 1973

Aspergillus and the production of citric acid

Citric acid is used in carbonated fruit drinks, e.g. lemonade, and in food flavouring. It is produced commercially by culturing *Aspergillus niger*.

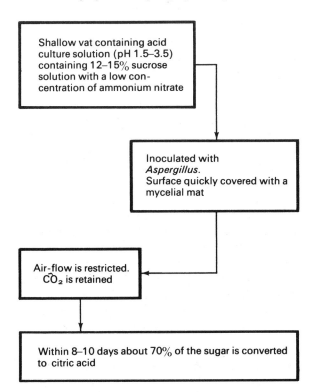

Shallow vat containing acid culture solution (pH 1.5–3.5) containing 12–15% sucrose solution with a low concentration of ammonium nitrate

↓

Inoculated with *Aspergillus*. Surface quickly covered with a mycelial mat

↓

Air-flow is restricted. CO_2 is retained

↓

Within 8–10 days about 70% of the sugar is converted to citric acid

Figure 5.41 The industrial production of citric acid by the action of *Aspergillus* can be carried out in versatile, stirred stainless steel fermenters

Courtesy of John and E. Sturge Ltd

Neurospora and the testing of the 'one gene one enzyme' hypothesis

Neurospora (the 'bakery mould' or 'red bread-mould') can infest bakeries and cause damage to flour stocks. *Neurospora crassa* can be grown in the laboratory on an agar medium (known as a 'minimal medium') containing cane sugar, inorganic salts and the vitamin biotin.

Neurospora has become an important experimental organism, used in investigations to test the hypothesis that genes act by directing the formation of specific enzymes (proteins). Its advantages for the research worker are:

(a) an extremely short life-cycle;

(b) only seven pairs of chromosomes on which the gene positions are easily mapped;

(c) a life-cycle in which the haploid state lasts for a long time and consequently recessive genes are immediately detectable;

(d) the ascospores occur in a linear series in the ascus and they can be dissected out to isolate individual reproductive progeny.

Working in the period 1941–1958, George Beadle and Edward Tatum exposed spores to X-rays and UV-light. When these spores were cultured, some of the mycelia produced could no longer grow on minimal medium. By adding extra growth factors or amino acids one by one it could be determined which substance a mutant fungus could no longer synthesise. Three strains of mutant *Neurospora* that could not survive on minimal medium were:

Mutant A, grew only when arginine was added;
Mutant B, grew when either arginine or citrulline was added;
Mutant C, grew when arginine, citrulline or ornithine was added.

Biochemists have shown that cells produce the amino acid arginine by the following pathway:

$$\text{precursor molecule} \xrightarrow[1]{\text{enzyme}} \text{ornithine} \xrightarrow[2]{\text{enzyme}} \text{citrulline} \xrightarrow[3]{\text{enzyme}} \text{arginine}$$

On the hypothesis that one gene is responsible for one enzyme, then:

Mutant A must have lost the gene for enzyme 3. The addition of ornithine or citrulline will not permit growth. Arginine added to the medium allows growth of the mutant.

Mutant B must have lost the gene for enzyme 2. The addition of either citrulline or arginine will permit growth.

Mutant C must have lost the gene for enzyme 1. The addition of any of the amino acids of the pathway supports growth.

These explanations were confirmed by,

(a) analysis of enzymes present in cells,

(b) by further breeding experiments.

Dutch Elm disease

For centuries the elm was an important feature of the British landscape, but since the late 1960s Dutch Elm disease has killed millions of elms and the tree has now virtually disappeared from the British countryside.

Dutch Elm disease is caused by a sac fungus (Ascomycete) called *Ceratocystis ulmi* which is carried from infected to healthy trees by specific bark-boring beetles. The spread of the disease is intimately tied-up with the life-cycle of these beetles.

The vector: bark beetles

Many species of insect can be contaminated with fungal spores but only bark beetles are common vectors of Dutch Elm disease because they move from diseased trees to healthy ones. The tunnels made by bark beetles and their larvae are better known than the beetles themselves. The bark of dead trees quickly falls, revealing these disused galleries.

Figure 5.44 Elm bark with bore holes

Chris Clegg

Beetles overwinter as fully grown larvae or as adults, and emerge from early April. They are attracted by the odour of diseased elms. Once arrived at a suitable host tree, the females attract breeding males by releasing into the air a pheromone. Then the female bores into the bark, followed by the male, and a tunnel is excavated in the cambium. Mating occurs and the female lays fertilised eggs at intervals along the main gallery. When the larvae hatch they tunnel at right angles, and the characteristic pattern of the galleries is produced. When mature, the larvae pupate under the bark and the adults later emerge from new exit holes.

The pathogen: *Ceratocystis ulmi*

Ceratocystis ulmi, the fungus that causes Dutch Elm disease, feeds on elm cells and lives in the galleries bored out by bark beetles. Two types of spores are formed (ascospores and conidiospores), both forms are transported from tree to tree on the bodies of insects.

Figure 5.42 Adult bark beetles and the galleries left by them and their larvae below the bark

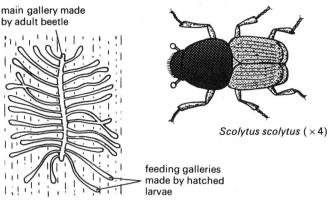

main gallery made by adult beetle

Scolytus scolytus (×4)

feeding galleries made by hatched larvae

Figure 5.43 The effects of *Ceratocystis ulmi* attack on elms

Gene Cox

These new adults fly to healthy elm trees and feed, transferring the fungus to the healthy elm from infected trees.

Figure 5.46 Scanning electron micrograph of the flask-shaped fruiting body of *Ceratocystis ulmi* having exuded a large sphere filled with ascospores (×150) ➤

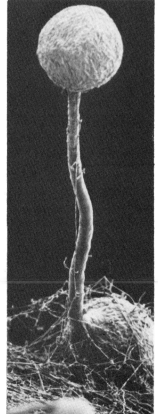

Figure 5.45 The life-cycle of *Ceratocystis ulmi*

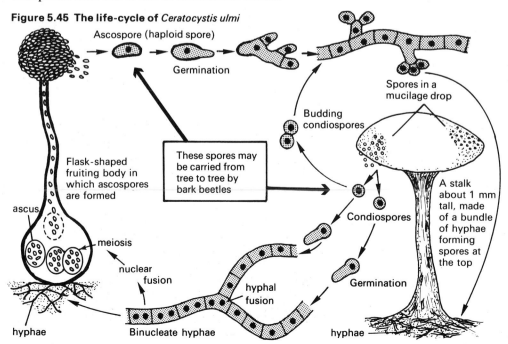

Ascospore (haploid spore)

Germination

Flask-shaped fruiting body in which ascospores are formed

These spores may be carried from tree to tree by bark beetles

Budding condiospores

Spores in a mucilage drop

ascus

meiosis

nuclear fusion

hyphal fusion

Condiospores

Germination

A stalk about 1 mm tall, made of a bundle of hyphae forming spores at the top

hyphae

Binucleate hyphae

hyphae

Figures 5.46, 47, 48. Miller, H. J. & D. M. Elgersma. *Neth. J. Plant Path.* 82: 51–65, 1976.

How the elm tree is killed

The symptoms of Dutch Elm disease begin with the wilting of leaves. These may turn yellow, become very dry, and quickly fall from the tree. Once the bark is scraped off, the outer wood can be seen to be dark-spotted and streaked. The healthy elm tree is most susceptible to infection whilst it is forming early (spring) wood from late May to early July.

The fungal hyphae grow in the xylem vessels and partially block them. The fungus secretes a toxin which changes the pit wall of the xylem vessels so that outgrowths (tyloses), from the surrounding xylem parenchyma, block the vessels completely.

Figure 5.47 Scanning electron micrographs of elm xylem showing the vessels and the numerous pits through which water travels laterally (× 600). The enlarged view shows a fungal hypha growing within the xylem vessel with a branch penetrating two pits (× 2000)

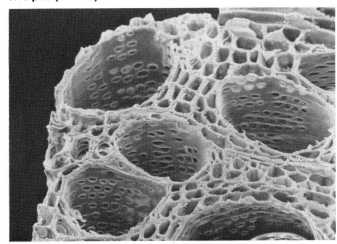
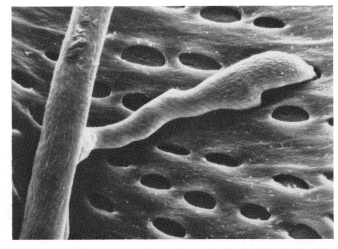

The history of Dutch Elm disease

Dutch Elm disease probably originated in Asia, but it was first reported in North West France in 1918. The first outbreak in the UK was reported in 1927. By the early 1930s it was widely reported all over Europe and had reached the USA. These outbreaks were severe, many trees died but some elm trees recovered and flourished. Slowly the incidence of the disease decreased. During the late 1960s severe outbreaks were again reported and this time there was no evidence of subsequent recovery. It is therefore believed that a new virulent strain of the fungus was causing the outbreak. Before the outbreak elms made up about 90% of hedgerow and field trees in lowland UK. By the end of 1978 15.5 million elms had died. The disease level in the north and west of Britain is lower. Many elm shoots (suckers) can be seen growing from the stumps of felled trees, but most are, as yet, too small to be attacked by bark boring beetles.

The prevention or cure of Dutch Elm disease, and the replacement of elms

Control of Dutch Elm disease may be possible by means of the following strategies.

1. Prompt felling of diseased elm trees.

2. Elimination of felled elm wood likely to be colonised by the beetles (these two are 'sanitation' measures which are practical only in isolated areas).

3. Use of systemic fungicides and insecticides sprayed onto vulnerable and infected trees (these measures are extremely expensive, and they contribute to the build up of dangerously persistent residues within the biosphere of poisons such as DDT); to preserve individual elms of unique beauty and position that would otherwise die.

4. Replacement of susceptible strains such as English Elm (*Ulmus procera*) and Wych Elm (*U. glabra*) with more resistant ones such as Cornish Elm (*U. stricta*) and Huntingdon Elm (*U. hollandica vegeta*). Asian species of elm have the greatest resistance but do not grow well in the UK.

5. New developments centre on attempts at biological control measures. For the bark beetles; these measures include controlling the males in the populations with artificial pheromones and releasing wasps which parasitise the beetles. For the fungus, control measures include inoculating infected trees with cultures of *Pseudomonas* spp that release antimycotics (antifungal chemicals).

Through these methods it is hoped that the spread of the infective organism can be checked.

Other vascular wilt diseases

Vascular wilt fungi enter their host plant through young roots, and feed on the cells of the cortex. Subsequently, they grow into the vascular tissue and the host plant is harmed by the mechanical plugging of xylem vessels and by the effects of toxins produced. The symptoms of infection are yellowing, withering and death of leaves. Examples are, *Fusarium oxysporum* var cubanse which causes Banana Wilt, *Fusarium solani* which causes Potato Wilt, *Verticillium* species which cause many other specific wilt diseases.

Figure 5.48 Scanning electron micrograph of xylem vessels and the hyphae of *Verticillium alboatrum* which causes Tomato Wilt (× 15 000)

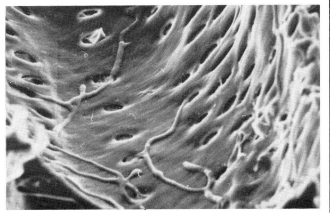

Dr. R. M. Cooper

Mushrooms

Common examples include the edible *Agaricus campestris* (Field Mushroom) and *A. arvensis* (Horse Mushroom). The names mushroom and toadstool have no precise scientific meaning; they are general names for the umbrella-shaped fruiting bodies that are particularly common in the months of September and October after heavy rain and under warm, humid conditions. The fungal mycelium grows in soil or wood throughout the year, and consists of colourless hyphae. The numerous hyphal fusions that occur convert the mycelium into a three-dimensional network. The mycelium absorbs nutrients and mobilises food reserves, concentrating these at points where a fruiting body is forming. Pores (see page 42) in the cross walls between each cell allow cytoplasm and food materials to flow along the hyphae. The fruiting body that develops looks solid but is built of these branching and interwoven hyphae, very closely packed together.

Figure 5.49 The formation and structure of a mushroom fruiting body

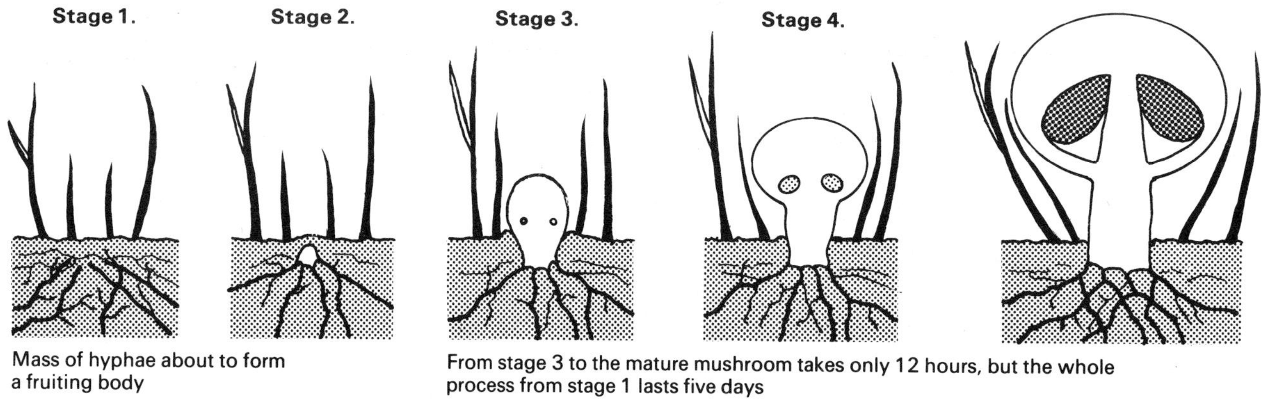

Stage 1.   Stage 2.   Stage 3.   Stage 4.   Stage 5.

Mass of hyphae about to form a fruiting body

From stage 3 to the mature mushroom takes only 12 hours, but the whole process from stage 1 lasts five days

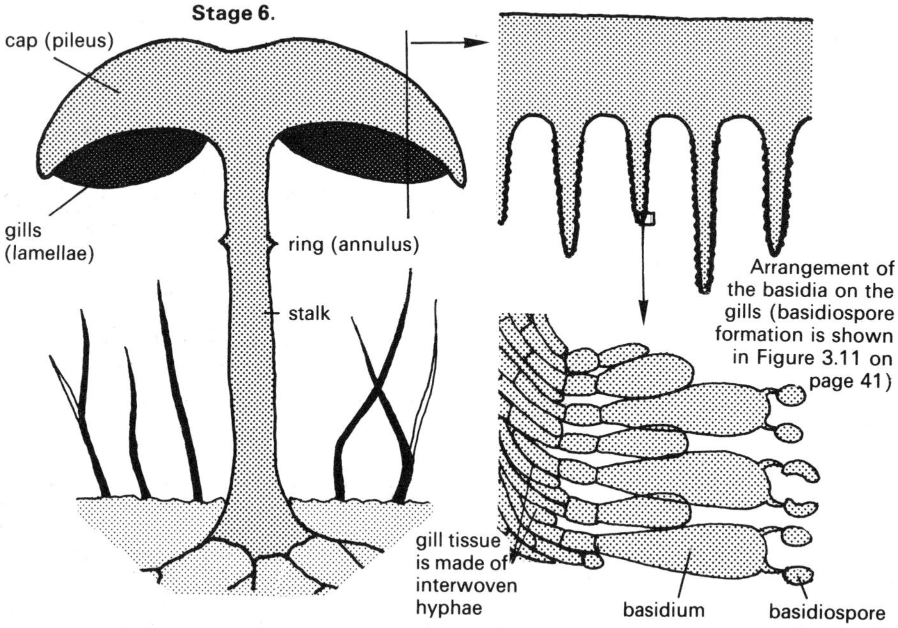

Stage 6.

cap (pileus)

gills (lamellae)   ring (annulus)

stalk

gill tissue is made of interwoven hyphae

Arrangement of the basidia on the gills (basidiospore formation is shown in Figure 3.11 on page 41)

basidium   basidiospore

Figure 5.50 Mature basidiospores

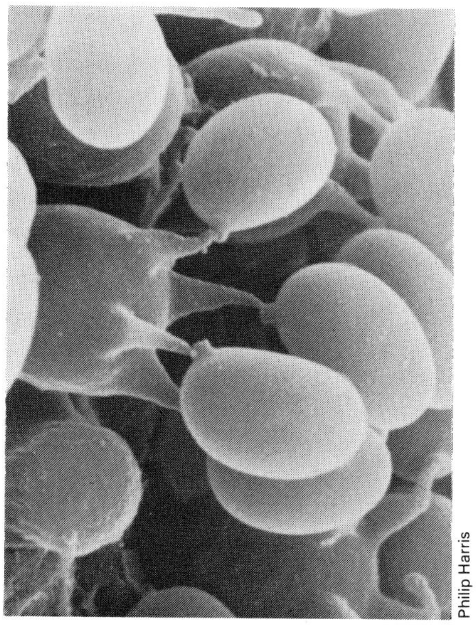

Philip Harris

Figure 5.51(i) Transverse section of the cap of *Agaricus* sp.

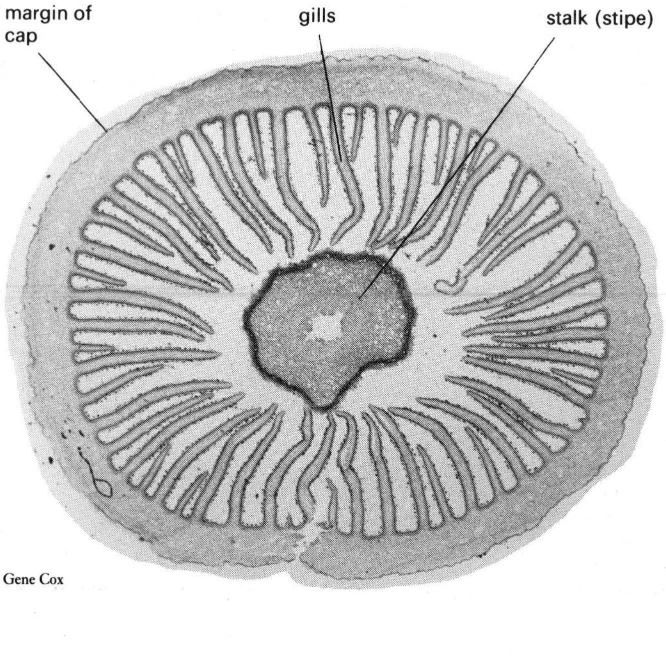

margin of cap   gills   stalk (stipe)

Gene Cox

Figure 5.51(ii) Transverse section of *Agaricus* sp. gill (× 400)

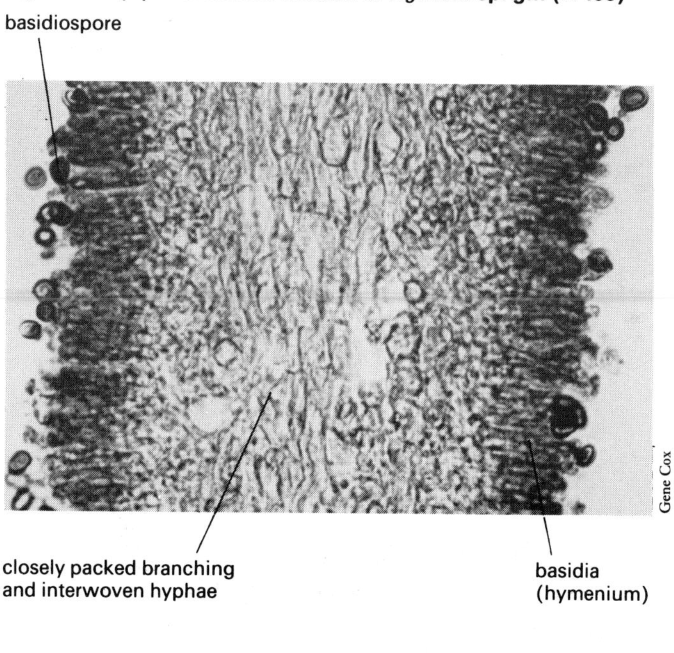

basidiospore

closely packed branching and interwoven hyphae

basidia (hymenium)

Gene Cox

The release and dispersal of spores

Four haploid basidiospores form at the tip of projections (sterigma) on the top of each basidium. Each basidiospore is shot violently away in turn, falls between the gills, and is then carried away by air currents. A Field Mushroom of about 8 cm diameter may discharge about 600 000 spores every minute for two days.

Figure 5.52 Stages in basidiospore release

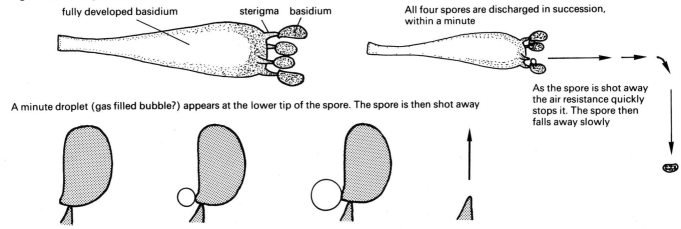

fully developed basidium   sterigma   basidium

All four spores are discharged in succession, within a minute

A minute droplet (gas filled bubble?) appears at the lower tip of the spore. The spore is then shot away

As the spore is shot away the air resistance quickly stops it. The spore then falls away slowly

Figure 5.53 The bubble-burst theory of basidiospore discharge, and a model to illustrate it

Adapted from Ingold, C. T. *The Nature of Toadstools*. Arnold Studies in Biology No. 113, 1979

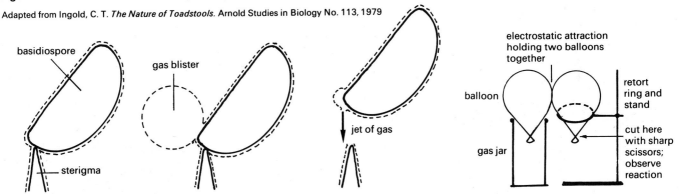

basidiospore

gas blister

jet of gas

sterigma

electrostatic attraction holding two balloons together

balloon

gas jar

retort ring and stand

cut here with sharp scissors; observe reaction

The spore is haploid, and on germination initially establishes a monokaryotic (one nucleus per cell) mycelium. This is a short-lived phase. Hyphal fusion with a compatible mycelium establishes dikaryotic mycelium (two nuclei per cell). From this the fruiting bodies eventually form. In the developing basidium, nuclear fusion is followed by meiosis. Thus, the basidiospores are haploid.

A summary of the life-cycle of *Agaricus* sp.

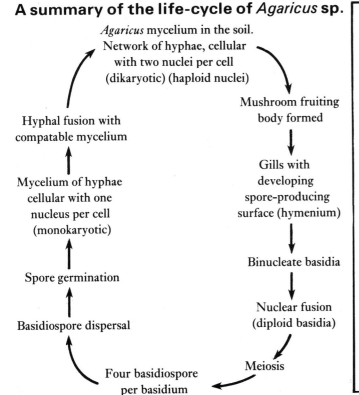

Agaricus mycelium in the soil. Network of hyphae, cellular with two nuclei per cell (dikaryotic) (haploid nuclei)

Hyphal fusion with compatable mycelium

Mycelium of hyphae cellular with one nucleus per cell (monokaryotic)

Spore germination

Basidiospore dispersal

Four basidiospore per basidium

Mushroom fruiting body formed

Gills with developing spore-producing surface (hymenium)

Binucleate basidia

Nuclear fusion (diploid basidia)

Meiosis

Making spore prints

Cut off the stalk from a freshly-opened cap of a gill-bearing fungus and place it, gills downwards, on glossy paper or a sheet of clear glass. After a few hours carefully lift away the cap. A system of radiating lines corresponding to the space between gills will be seen, marked out in millions of white, buff, brown, pink, purple or black spores, depending on the species of mushroom. The print can be made permanent by spraying with non-inflammable matt lacquer.

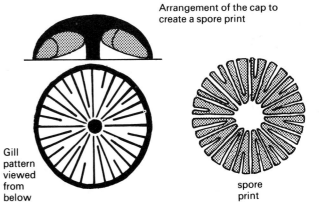

Arrangement of the cap to create a spore print

Gill pattern viewed from below

spore print

Fairy-rings

Fairy-rings are those circles of dark green grass seen on lawns or any closely cut meadow. They may be a few to many feet across. Originally the mycelium was established at the centre, and has grown outwards forming a circular colony, but dying back behind. Where the mycelium is actively colonizing new soil there are nitrogenous chemicals released and the grass is dark green. Immediately behind this zone the mycelium dominates the soil, the grass is poorer, and the ring of mushrooms appears in autumn.

Figure 5.54 The Fairy-ring Fungus, *Marasmius oreades,* **and how the ring is formed**

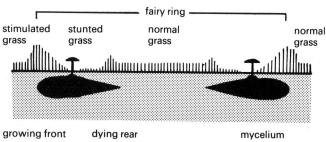

Universal veil

Some mushrooms are protected by a 'universal veil' as they develop. As the fruiting body enlarges the veil tears to leave a cup at the base. The remains of the veil are visible as scales on the cap.

Figure 5.55 Development of the universal veil of *Amanita muscaria*

Figure 5.56 Fly Agaric Fungus (*Amanita muscaria***)**

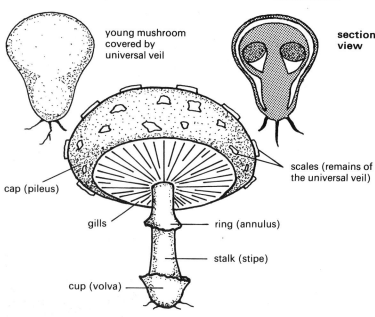

The Shaggy Ink-cap Mushroom (*Coprinus comatus*)

In the gills of this fungus, there is a gradient of development of the spores. At the lower tip of the gills, the cap and gills autodigest once the spores have been discharged.

Figure 5.57(i) The structure and function of the Shaggy Ink-cap Mushroom

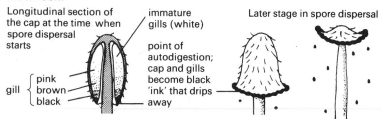

Figure 5.57(ii) The Shaggy Ink-cap Mushroom (*Coprinus comatus***) (× 0.5)**

Edible and poisonous fungi

Several fungi are very good to eat; several are either deadly poisonous or they have unpleasant effects. The majority of fungi are harmless but worthless as food. Anyone considering eating wild mushrooms should identify and learn to recognise all mushrooms and toadstools they find.

Books for further reading include, M. Lange and F. B. Hora. *Collins Guide to Mushrooms and Toadstools.* Collins, 1978. R. Phillips. *Mushrooms and other Fungi of Great Britain and Europe.* Pan, 1981.

Polypores and other tube mushrooms

Some fleshy mushrooms produce basidiospores in vertical tubes which open below by pores, rather than on radiating gills.

Figure 5.58 Basidiospore production in the pores of Slippery Jack Mushroom (*Suillus luteus*)

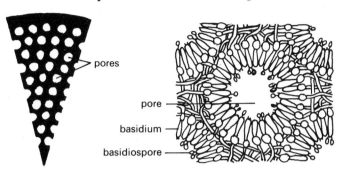

View of the lower surface of the cap

High magnification showing detail of the spores

pores

pore

basidium

basidiospore

Shelf-like bracket fungi

Most polyporus fungi exist as bracket or shelf fungi growing from the trunks or branches of living, dying, or dead trees. These fruiting bodies last longer than fleshy mushrooms, and many discharge spores over many weeks. Most last for only one season, but a few are perennial.

Figure 5.59 Bracket fungi (*Polyporus betulinus*) seen on a dead birch tree (× 0.3)

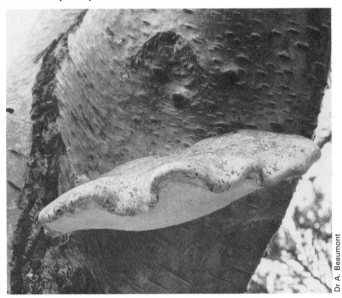

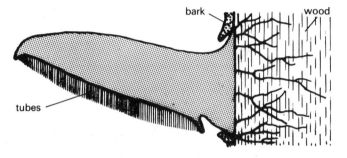

bark

wood

tubes

Fairy Clubs

Fairy clubs are erect, fleshy club-like fruiting bodies that produce basidiospores over the exposed surface.

Figure 5.60 *Clavulinopsis helvola*, a Fairy Club (× 0.6)

Earth-balls

Earth-balls are fungus fruiting bodies in which the spores are contained within a tough, warty sphere. The spores are released, when the skin cracks open, and blown, carried or splashed away.

Figure 5.61(i) Common Earth-ball (*Scleroderma citrinium*) (× 0.5). The fruiting body has been broken open to reveal the spore mass coloured purple-black, surrounded by a thick wall

Figure 5.61(ii) Common Earth-ball

Fungi and trees

Many fungi are particularly associated with woods and trees, and whilst some species grow on, or with, a wide range of trees, many other species of fungus are restricted to particular species of tree. The feeding relationship may be saprophytic, parasitic or mycorrhizal.

Figure 5.62 Trees, and some common fungi which associate with them

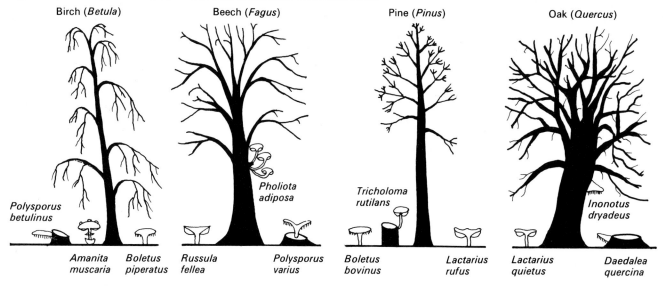

Birch (*Betula*) Beech (*Fagus*) Pine (*Pinus*) Oak (*Quercus*)

Polysporus betulinus *Pholiota adiposa* *Tricholoma rutilans* *Inonotus dryadeus*

Amanita muscaria Boletus piperatus Russula fellea Polysporus varius Boletus bovinus Lactarius rufus Lactarius quietus Daedalea quercina

Saprophytes and trees

Saprophytes are plants that obtain their nutrition from decaying matter.

Figure 5.63 Coral Spot Fungus (*Nectria cinnabarina*) (Life size)

The Coral Spot Fungus is extremely common on a wide range of different types of dead branch or twig. Coral pink bodies push through the dead bark and the conidia formed on them are dispersed by splashing rain drops.

Figure 5.64 Sulphur Tuft Fungus (*Hypholoma fasciculare*) (× 0.3)
The Sulphur Tuft Fungus grows on logs and stumps of both broad-leaved and coniferous trees.

Figure 5.65 *Pleurotus cornucopiea* on a dead elm trunk, also colonised by the lichen *Cladonia fimriata*, next to the bore holes of the bark beetle *Scolytus* sp. (Life size)

Pleurotus cornucopiea forms clusters of fruiting bodies which burst through dead bark. This fungus has deeply recurrent gills (attached down the stalk). The fruiting body is cream coloured, but the spore print is pale lilac.

Parasites and trees

Parasites feed on a living host organism and live in or on their host for the greater part of their life-cycle.

The Honey, or Bootlace, Fungus spreads from infected trees by long black cords (rhyzomorphs), resembling bootlaces which grow from the trunk or roots, through the soil for many metres to infect other trees. There is no cure; this fungus is one of the most dangerous parasites of trees. It feeds on the cambium region of trunks, roots and branches of most species.

Figure 5.66 Honey, or Bootlace Fungus (*Armillaria mellea*) (× 0.3)

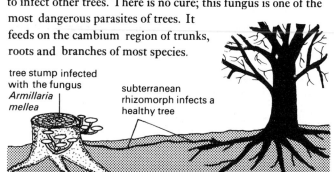

tree stump infected with the fungus *Armillaria mellea*

subterranean rhizomorph infects a healthy tree

Mycorrhiza

1. Ectotrophic

The majestic, apparently self-contained, forest and woodland trees live mutualistically with certain species of soil-inhabiting fungi. The fungal hyphae enclose the trees rootlets with a compact sheath, and hyphae penetrate between the cells of the cortex as well as extending far out into the soil. The relationship is a nutritional alliance. The tree supplies the fungus with sugar and using the sugar as an energy source hyphae reach out into the soil many metres from the tree. These fungal hyphae (a functional replacement for the root-hairs) absorb precious ions from the soil wherever and whenever they are available, and leak them back to the tree as it requires them, particularly during the spring. This nutritional interdependence has been investigated experimentally with radioactively labelled tracers. The relationship is known as ectotrophic mycorrhiza. Mycorrhizal roots are much branched, but short and stunted when compared with non-infected roots of the trees. The trees involved in this relationship include pine, spruce, larch, firs, oak, beech and birch. The species of fungus commonly associated with trees via ectotrophic mycorrhiza include members of the *Amanita*, *Russula*, *Boletus* and *Lactarius* genera.

Figure 5.67 Experimental investigation of the nutritional alliance of ectotrophic mycorrhiza

Air containing $^{14}CO_2$ made available to the leaves in the light

inverted glass jar with stand

radioactively labelled inorganic ions appear in the tree tissue

young Scots Pine plant

radioactive sugar quickly appears in fungal hyphae in the soil

culture of mycorrhizal fungus supplied with inorganic nutrients (nitrates, phosphates, or potassium) that are radioactively labelled

translocation of materials in the plant stem

bung

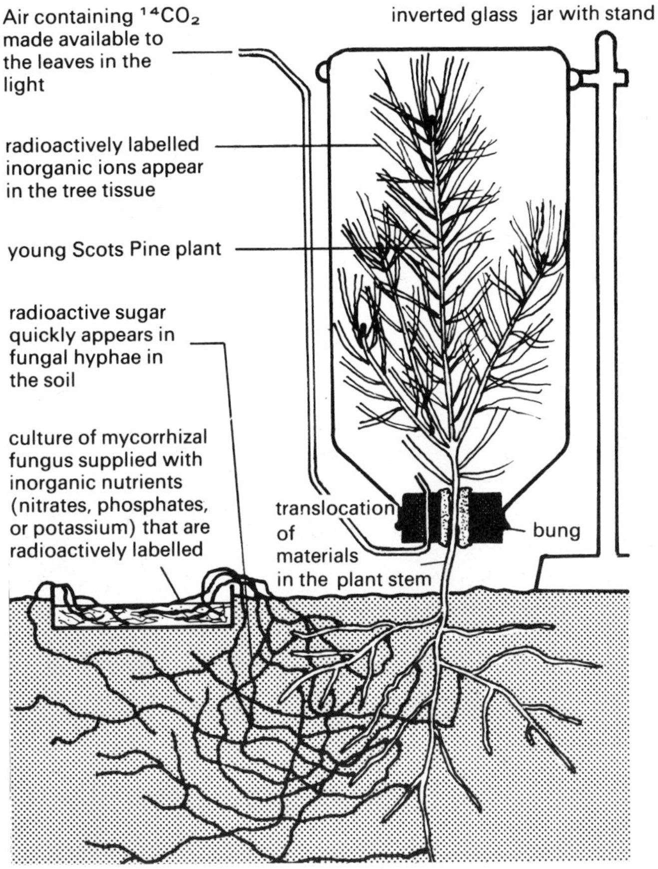

Figure 5.68 The structure and function of ectotrophic mycorrhiza

mycorrhizal root

Lateral root

normal root tips with root hairs

Mycorrhizal root in section

fungal hypha

xylem

ectotrophic mycorrhizal sheath

phloem

hyphae between the cells of the cortex (exchange of sugars and ions between the fungus and the tree occurs here)

Hyphae in contact with the soil particles and soil solution (absorption of ions occurs)

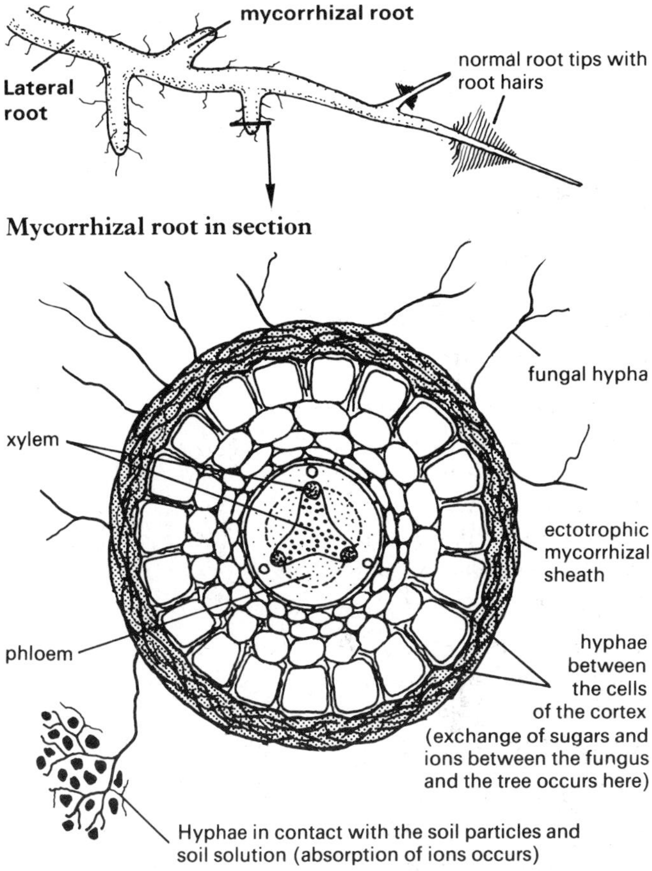

2. Endotrophic

There are also many examples of endotrophic mycorrhiza known. Here the fungus actually penetrates into the tissue and cells of the host. Orchids have this relationship, as do heathers growing on heathland. Orchid seeds are 'infested' with the fungus as they form on the plant, and the seeds contain little or no food reserves. The developing plant obtains nutrients saprophytically by digesting the fungal hyphae and releasing food from the fungus. Meanwhile, the fungal hyphae feed saprophytically outside the host root. The products of digestion reach the host plant as well as the fungus. The infection of the host cells is limited and release of the food facilitated by repeated digestion of the fungus as it re-invades the host cells.

Figure 5.69 Orchid root tissue in section, showing hyphae of endotrophic mycorrhiza

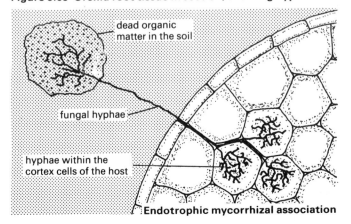

dead organic matter in the soil

fungal hyphae

hyphae within the cortex cells of the host

Endotrophic mycorrhizal association

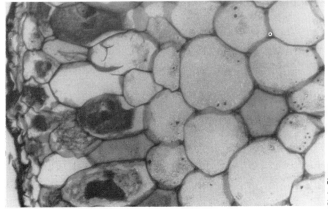

Chris Clegg

Spore dispersal in fungi

Spores are liberated before they are dispersed. Liberation may be passive, as in *Rhizopus* spp (page 45) and *Penicillium* spp (page 50), since they are merely exposed for dispersal, or it may be active by some explosive or violent discharge mechanism. Examples of the latter include basidiospores that are shot off the top of basidia (page 55), ascospores that are shot out of asci (page 40), and *Pilobolus* sp. where the whole sporangium is shot away (page 45).

Dispersal of fungal spores is usually by wind and air currents, for example, *Peronospora* conidia (page 40), *Rhizopus* spores (page 42), *Penicillium* and *Aspergillus* (page 50) and *Agaricus* (page 54).

There are exceptions to air-borne dispersal. Examples already described include dispersal by:

(a) insects: *Ceratocystis ulmi* by the bark beetle *Scolytus* spp (page 52) and *Mucor hiemalis* by the feet of flies (page 43),

(b) larger animals: coprophilous fungi (page 44),

(c) water drops: *Mucor hiemalis* (page 43) and *Nectria cinnabarina* (page 58).

Other examples of spore dispersal mechanisms

1. Dispersal of Common Stinkhorn (*Phallus impudicus*) spores by the actions of flies

The common stinkhorn grows in damp woodland; their fruiting bodies can usually be smelt before they are seen. Overnight the body develops to the 'egg' stage. The following morning the stalk elongates, the slime of the tip gives off the strong smell of rotting meat, and by noon the spores have been dispersed by flies.

Figure 5.70 Development of the fruiting body of the Common Stinkhorn (*Phallus impudicus*)

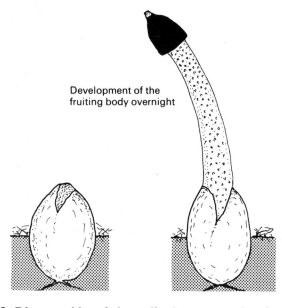

Development of the fruiting body overnight

Figure 5.71(i) Common Stinkhorn with ripe fruiting body

Figure 5.71(ii) Common Stinkhorn fruiting body after the spores have been dispersed by flies (×0.3)

Dr A. Beaumont

2. Dispersal by violent discharge mechanism

Sphaerobolus is a common saprophyte of old, rotten wood. The tiny fruiting bodies develop clustered together, each about 2 mm across. Initially, they are circular and cream-coloured, later they turn light brown and star-shaped in outline. As the cup dries out it is seen to contain a ball of spores (glebal mass). During drying the inner layer of the wall splits away from the outer layer, except at the rim. Suddenly, the inside wall turns inside out, catapulting the spore mass to a distance of several metres.

Figure 5.72 *Sphaerobolus stellatus* fruiting body structure and the dispersal of the spore mass

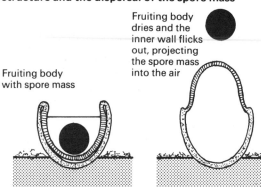

Fruiting body dries and the inner wall flicks out, projecting the spore mass into the air

Fruiting body with spore mass

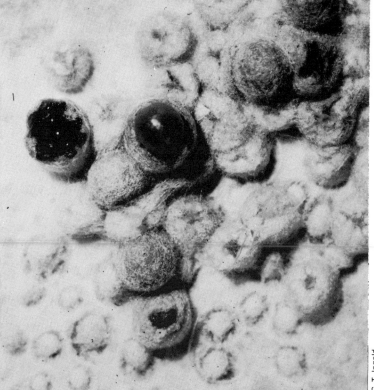

C. T. Ingold

3. Dispersal by the puffball

Puffballs form on the ground, attached by foot-like mycelial cords. The outer wall is dry, leathery and warty, and eventually cracks open. Within, is a dry, powdery spore mass. Eventually the puffball may break free, and be rolled, blown or carried about, dispersing spores. Also, large water drops, falling from trees above, may hit the leathery coat and cause a cloud of spores to be shot out.

4. Dispersal from Common Bird's Nest Fungi *Crucibulum* sp.

In these fungi a cup-shaped fruiting body contains a few egg-shaped packages of spores each contained within a wall of woven hyphae and connected to the fruiting body wall by a hyphal strand.
Any large water droplets that land in the cups, reflect the spore packages away for a metre or so. The attached hyphal strand is mucilaginous and may help the spore package to become attached to surrounding grass.

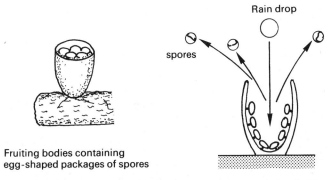

Fruiting bodies containing egg-shaped packages of spores

Figure 5.74 Common Bird's Nest Fungus *Crucibulum* sp. (×5)

Figure 5.73 Fruiting body of a puffball discharging spores (life size)

C. T. Ingold

Dr A. Beaumont

The rhizomorph; an additional strategy for dispersal

By means of rhizomorphs, the Honey Fungus (*Armillaria mellea*) may traverse many metres of open soil to attack new host trees (see page 58). The fungus *Merulius lachrymans*, which causes dry-rot of house timbers, produces vast numbers of air-borne basidiospores, but it also sends out rhizomorphs of interwoven hyphae which are capable of growing over dry plaster, brickwork and dry timber, and of causing a fresh attack if it reaches wet timbers. The effective preventative measure is to ensure that timbers are dry and well ventilated; the fungus can only feed and grow on permanently wet timbers rapidly reducing them to dry powder, once it is established.

Figure 5.75 The fruiting body of the Dry-Rot Fungus *Merulius lachrymans* with rhizomorphs

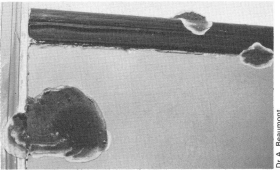

Dr A. Beaumont

Fungi and disease

Fungal pathogens are of great significance, causing disease in many plants including food crops, and so having an indirect effect upon Man. Only a few fungal pathogens have a direct effect upon Man.

Fungal diseases

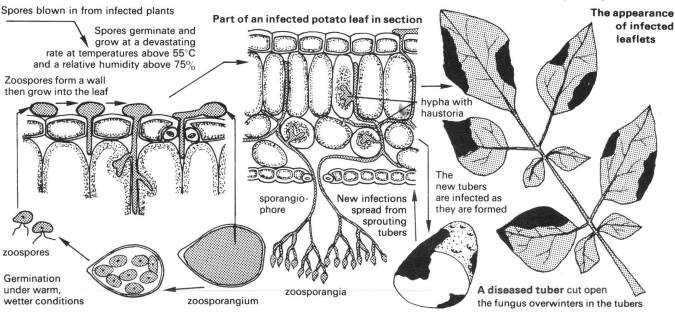

Farmer's Lung and related diseases caused by the fungi of mouldy plant products

Fungal spores in the air we breath can inflame the lung tissue, causing the lungs to produce excess mucus, leading to rapid, shallow breathing, coughing, and a rapid heart beat. Repeated exposure to high densities of fungal spores can lead to lung damage and heart failure. Air inhaled by workers opening bales of mouldy hay has been found to contain as many as 1600 million microbial spores per cubic metre. Normally hay is reduced to 20–25% water, but occasionally it is wrongly baled at 35% moisture, leading to total loss as mouldy compost.
Microbial spoilage leads to the following problems:

(a) reduced nutritional value,

(b) irritation by spores when the product is handled,

(c) some of the spores of fungi that cause high temperature decay are from organisms that are respiratory tract pathogens of poultry

Apart from these problems, mycotoxins are produced by many fungi, including those commonly occurring in animal foodstuffs, for example, *Aspergillus*, *Penicillium*, and *Fusarium* species. If stable, potent toxins are allowed to build up in livestock through the feeding of microbially-spoilt foodstuffs, there is also great danger for Man, positioned as he is at the top of agricultural food webs.

Figure 5.76 Sporing heads of *Aspergillus fumigatus,* **a common saprophyte of mouldy hay that has over-heated. This organism is a pathogen of poultry (× 450)**

Biophoto Associates/Gordon Leedale

Potato Blight (*Phytophthora infestans*)

Phytophthora infestans is an obligate parasite of the potato. It overwinters in infected tubers and the mycelium feeds upon the new plant and then produces sporangia. Provided conditions are wet and warm these sporangia result in many plants becoming infected.

Figure 5.77 *Phytophthora infestans*: **its cycle of asexual reproduction and infestation of the aerial parts of new potato plants**

Spores blown in from infected plants

Spores germinate and grow at a devastating rate at temperatures above 55°C and a relative humidity above 75%

Zoospores form a wall then grow into the leaf

Part of an infected potato leaf in section

The appearance of infected leaflets

hypha with haustoria

sporangio-phore

New infections spread from sprouting tubers

The new tubers are infected as they are formed

zoospores

Germination under warm, wetter conditions

zoosporangium

zoosporangia

A diseased tuber cut open the fungus overwinters in the tubers

Potato blight was first recorded in the British Isles in 1845 when it decimated the Irish potato crop of that year and caused the notorious Irish Famine. Since then, in warmer wetter areas of the country, the disease has caused persistent and severe damage to the potato crop.

Today Bordeaux mixture is sprayed on potato plants to control the spread of the disease. This is an aqueous mixture of copper sulphate and lime (calcium hydroxide) which, when sprayed onto leaves, becomes a suspension of insoluble copper hydroxide on the cuticle. Fungal hyphae give out small quantities of organic acid as they grow, and these acids react to release soluble, poisonous copper ions that quickly kill the fungus. Rain washes away the Bordeaux mixture. Spraying must be repeated if the disease spores are known to be in the area and conditions for growth are favourable.

Brown rot of apples and other fruits

This disease is caused by the entry of the fungus *Monilia fructigena* into apples whilst still on the trees or during storage. Entry is via breaks in the waxy skin. The tissue turns brown and then conidia are formed on the surface on discrete conidial cushions. Conidia are dispersed by birds, insects (e.g. fruit flies, flies and wasps), in air currents and through handling.

Figure 5.78 Brown rot of apples caused by *Monilia fructigena*, and showing the conidial cushions

Powdery mildews

Powdery mildews are plant diseases caused by fungi of the genus *Erysiphe* and related genera. They are some of the most commonly seen plant diseases. They affect over 7000 species of angiosperms. Leaf surfaces and stems become covered with an off-white weft of mycelium, all thickly dusted with powdery conidia. They may be confused with the downy mildews (e.g. *Peronospora*, see page 40) which always require cool, wet conditions in order to spread whereas powdery mildews are favoured by warm, dry weather. In summer and autumn many hedgerow plants can be seen infected. Crop parasites of this type include:

(a) powdery mildew of beet, *Erysiphe betae*, which can cause a yield loss of up to 25%,

(b) powdery mildew of barley, *Erysiphe graminis hordei*, which may attack 95–100% of spring-barley plants (winter-barley is little affected) with yield loss of 5–10%.

Fungicides used to combat these diseases are *either* surface-acting, such as Bordeaux mixture, with heavy and regular applications to protect new leaves and combat rain losses; *or* chemicals which, when sprayed onto the plant are absorbed through the leaves or roots and are transported around the plant in the xylem vessels to the growing point and to the leaves. These are called systemic fungicides; their effects persist, and the plant is protected from infection. Systemic fungicides are compounds based on the pyrimidine group. When a conidium lands on the leaf surface a haustorium is rapidly formed in a host cell, and once established the colony spreads over the leaf surface, attacking other cells and producing conidia.

Figure 5.79 The process of powdery mildew infection

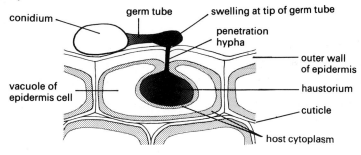

Rusts

The rusts are plant parasites of great economic importance. *Puccinia graminis* (black-rust of wheat) causes great damage to wheat production in North America. In this fungus there are five different types of spore in the life-cycle and there are two host plants. There are other rust and smut fungi.

Figure 5.80 Summary of the life cycle of *Puccinia graminis*: the fungus shown in and on the leaves of its host plants wheat and barberry

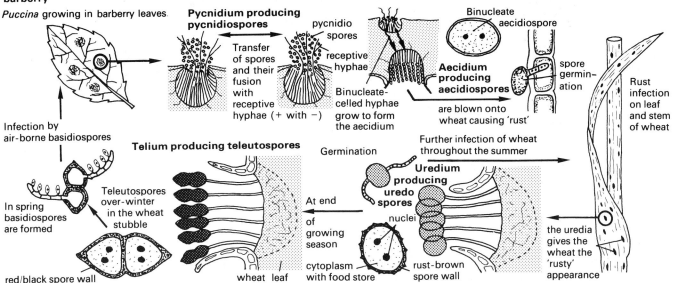

Lichens

Lichens are dual organisms. The thallus (a plant body not differentiated into a root and shoot) is made of two components, a fungus and an alga, living together as a self-supporting unit. There are several thousand different species of lichen, occurring in unusual, unfavourable and often quite hostile habitats. The structure of the lichen does not resemble the component organisms, where they may be observed living independently. The fungal component (known as the mycobiont) is almost always a member of the sac fungi (Ascomycetes, see page 40). Compact fungal hyphae make up the bulk of the lichen, providing its form and outline. The hyphae absorb and retain water and ions, when these are available, and they protect the algal cells from exposure. When the mycobiont is isolated and cultured free from the algal partner, it forms a structureless mass; the fungus requires the alga to survive and develop to maturity.

The algal component (known as the phycobiont) is either a green alga (e.g. *Chlorella*, *Pleurococcus*, see page 22) or a blue-green alga (e.g. *Nostoc*, see page 16). When the lichen is moist the alga manufactures sugar by photosynthesis, and any excess passes through the walls to the fungal hyphae and is used by the fungus for growth or stored in the hyphae. The lichen thallus grows very slowly but it is able to survive long periods of desiccation and extremes of temperature in exposed habitats where the supply of water and nutrients is only sporadic.

Most lichens have no common name; they are given Latin generic and specific names and these are largely determined by the mycobiont component.

Taxonomists recognise lichens as fungi that have become modified by an association with specific algae.

Figure 6.1 A selection of lichens growing on an exposed wooden gate post. Lichens are able to remain anchored and grow slowly in exposed habitats where water supply is sporadic and there is extreme temperature fluctuation

C. Clegg

Form of the lichen thallus

There is considerable variety of form within the lichens, but there are three common forms of the thallus recognised.

Crustose	crust-like, living closely attached to rock or stone (see Figure 6.2).
Foliose	leaf-like, attached to soil, plants or rock by root-like (fungal) threads (see Figure 6.4).
Fruticose	shrubby (erect) or beard-like (pendant), with a single point of attachment to the substratum (see Figure 6.3).

In addition, many species of lichens are intermediate between these basic forms.

Figure 6.2 Crustose lichens on rocks on the seashore which grow at or above the splash zone (× 0.5)

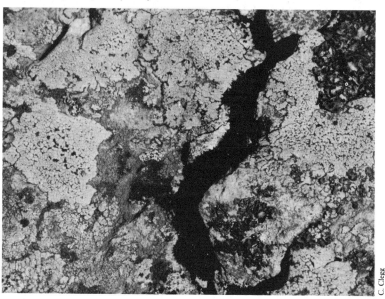

C. Clegg

Figure 6.3 Fruticose lichens of the genus *Usnea* (beard lichen), growing on a tree trunk (Life size)

Howard Jay

Figure 6.4 Foliose lichen of the genus *Parmelia* (Life size)

The structure of the lichen thallus

In a few species of lichen the internal structure of the thallus may be very simple, consisting of loosely interwoven fungal hyphae with algal cells scattered throughout the thallus.

Vertical section of a simple thallus,
e.g. *Collema* spp and *Leptogium* spp

Vertical section of a layered
thallus, e.g. *Xanthoria* spp

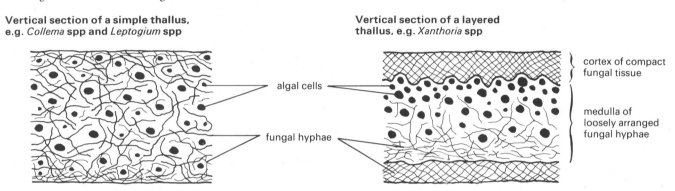

algal cells

fungal hyphae

cortex of compact fungal tissue

medulla of loosely arranged fungal hyphae

Most lichens have a layered structure with an upper and lower surface of compact fungal tissue and, between these, a layer of loosely arranged fungal hyphae with the algal cells concentrated just below the upper cortex.

Figure 6.5 Vertical section of the lichen *Xanthoria* sp. The thallus is foliose and grows on rocks, walls, roofs, trees and fences. The thallus is bright orange

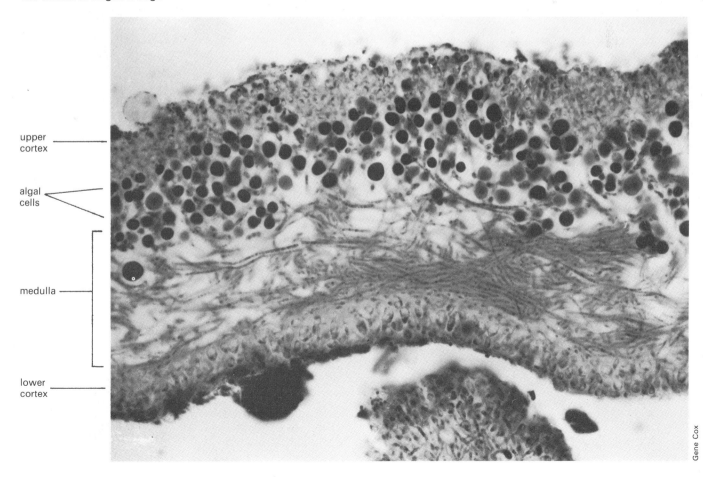

upper cortex

algal cells

medulla

lower cortex

Reproduction

Many lichens produce tiny, powdery clumps of algal cells enveloped in fungal hyphae (called a soredium). These appear over the whole surface of the thallus, or on a specialised part called a soralium.

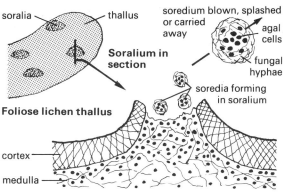

Soredia are blown, splashed or carried away unintentionally by passing animals, and may eventually develop into new lichen plants.

Sexual reproduction of the mycobiont occurs by the production of ascospores in asci and their violent discharge and dispersal in the air. Asci are produced in cup-shaped apothecium, or flask-shaped perithecium, reproductive bodies on the thallus. (This form of reproduction is typical of the sac-fungi; see page 40.) When the fungal spores have reached a new habitat they must contact and associate with algal cells at the new site in order to produce a new lichen plant. The distribution of lichens confirms the efficiency of their reproductive mechanism; most species show world-wide distribution.

Figure 6.6 The lichen *Xanthoria* sp. in surface view and section, showing apothecia in which ascospores are produced in asci

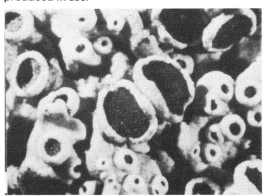

Gene Cox

cup-shaped sexual reproductive bodies (apothecia), in surface view

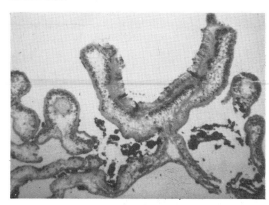

Gene Cox

apothecium in section: asci produce and discharge ascospores here

Figure 6.7 The lichen *Cladonia pityrea* growing on acid heathland beside moss of the genus *Polytrichum*. Soredia are produced all over the foliose thallus; apothecia are on stalks growing to a height of 1–2 centimetres above the thallus

Polytrichum sp. moss

stalked apothecium producing ascospores

foliose thallus of *Cladonia* sp. growing on soil/peat surface

C. Clegg

Physiology of lichen mutualism

Rain water and condensation, with dissolved chemicals, are absorbed over the whole thallus

SUNLIGHT

Water evaporates away in hot, dry or windy conditions. There is no protection from desiccation: the cortex of the thallus has no cuticle

When the thallus is moist, photosynthesis and respiration occur rapidly. When the thallus dries these processes are slowed down

Many lichens produce lichen acid which may become deposited on the thallus surface as crystals. Some lichen acids are colourless, others are brightly coloured. Coloured acids are common on lichens fully exposed to intense sunlight: they may protect the thallus from excess light or heat

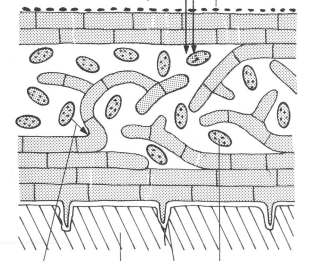

Excess carbohydrates (glucose and sugar-alcohols, e.g. ribitol) pass through the walls to the fungal hyphae, where they are turned into mannitol and used for growth; any excess is stored

Substratum to which lichen anchors

When the phycobiont is a blue-green alga, the cells can fix atmospheric nitrogen and accumulate nitrates and amino acids. These too reach the fungus

Hyphae grow into tiny cracks and anchor the lichen thallus

Ecology

Lichens compete poorly against larger plants. They occur mostly as primary colonisers, able to hold on and survive where other organisms cannot. Their habitats include the rocky shore, mountain summits, hot deserts, the arctic and antarctic, as well as stems, trunks of trees, the soil, fence posts and rocks. On rock surfaces they may contribute to the early formation of soil, following weathering of rock to mineral fragments. Lichen remains may provide the first organic input to the soil.

Figure 6.8 Section through a rock profile to show the role of colonising lichens in the sequence of erosion and soil formation

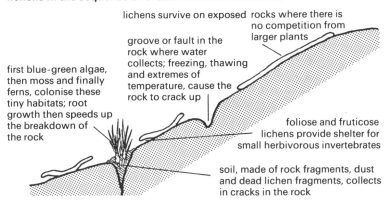

lichens survive on exposed rocks where there is no competition from larger plants

groove or fault in the rock where water collects; freezing, thawing and extremes of temperature, cause the rock to crack up

first blue-green algae, then moss and finally ferns, colonise these tiny habitats; root growth then speeds up the breakdown of the rock

foliose and fruticose lichens provide shelter for small herbivorous invertebrates

soil, made of rock fragments, dust and dead lichen fragments, collects in cracks in the rock

Lichens as pollution indicators

Lichens and bryophytes (see pages 68–73) are especially susceptible to any air-borne pollutants dissolved in rainwater that may reach them. These terrestrial plants have no cuticle, whereas the aerial parts of higher plants are protected by a continuous waxy cuticle, and the plants absorb water and ions from the soil via their roots.

Ecological and Economic aspects

Lichens play an important role in some habitats. In arctic regions and on barren moorlands lichens provide food for large herbivorous mammals such as deer, reindeer and caribou herds during the long winter months.

From certain species of *Cladonia* growing in Scandinavia and Northern Europe the yellow pigment usnic acid is obtained. It is used as a cheap, effective broad-spectrum antibiotic in ointments applied to large external wounds, such as burns. In addition, the dyes used to colour Harris Tweeds and the common laboratory acid–base indicator litmus are also obtained from lichens.

Figure 6.9 Two lichens common on moorland, seen growing between heather and bilberry plants.
The more wire-like *Cladonia portentosa* is a species eaten by deer in winter. The broader *Hypogymnia physodes* is a species used as an indicator species in air pollution surveys

C. Clegg

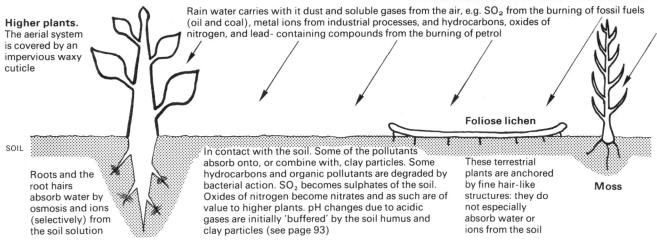

Higher plants. The aerial system is covered by an impervious waxy cuticle

Rain water carries with it dust and soluble gases from the air, e.g. SO_2 from the burning of fossil fuels (oil and coal), metal ions from industrial processes, and hydrocarbons, oxides of nitrogen, and lead- containing compounds from the burning of petrol

Foliose lichen

SOIL

In contact with the soil. Some of the pollutants absorb onto, or combine with, clay particles. Some hydrocarbons and organic pollutants are degraded by bacterial action. SO_2 becomes sulphates of the soil. Oxides of nitrogen become nitrates and as such are of value to higher plants. pH changes due to acidic gases are initially 'buffered' by the soil humus and clay particles (see page 93)

Roots and the root hairs absorb water by osmosis and ions (selectively) from the soil solution

These terrestrial plants are anchored by fine hair-like structures: they do not especially absorb water or ions from the soil

Moss

Lichens and mosses are used to investigate the extent and nature of air-borne pollution.

Samples of the lichen *Evernia pruastri* found on trees (windward side of the trunk) were carefully observed at increasing distances from the centre of a large industrial conurbation (in the case shown below this was Newcastle-upon-Tyne). Studies showed that the thallus was progressively reduced in size at sites nearer the city centre, and this reduction could be correlated to mean winter sulphur dioxide (SO_2) pollution varying between 170 $\mu g/m^3$ of air at the centre, to less than 50 $\mu g/m^3$ of air 30 km from the centre.

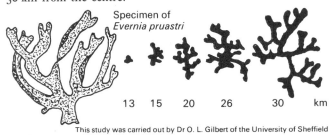

Specimen of *Evernia pruastri*

13   15   20   26   30   km

This study was carried out by Dr O. L. Gilbert of the University of Sheffield

Lichens absorb and accumulate various pollutants and plant samples can be collected and analysed periodically to indicate the extent of the contamination by metal ions from industrial sources.

Figure 6.10 Graph of the concentration of various metals in the lichen *Peltigera rufescens* in parts per million (ppm) dry weight, from sites up to 3 km from a steel works

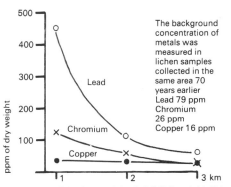

The background concentration of metals was measured in lichen samples collected in the same area 70 years earlier
Lead 79 ppm
Chromium 26 ppm
Copper 16 ppm

Lead

Chromium

Copper

ppm of dry weight

500
400
300
200
100

1   2   3 km

(Both these studies are reported in: Hawksworth, D. L. and Rose, F. *Lichens as Pollution Monitors*. Arnold Studies in Biology, 66, 1976)

This study was carried out by Dr R. M. Seward of the University of Bradford

Mosses and liverworts (Bryophytes)

Bryophytes are small, green plants that usually grow exclusively on the land in permanently moist situations. They are commonly known as mosses and liverworts. The plant body has either a simple, slender, relatively weak stem with whorls or rows of small, simple, delicate leaves, or it consists of a green thallus of leaf-like tissue growing on the ground. Bryophytes have no waxy cuticle protecting the aerial system from water loss. The plant is anchored to the substratum by delicate, colourless or brown outgrowths from the cells of the lower surface called rhizoids. The plants do not have roots. Bryophytes absorb water all over their plant body and not exclusively from the soil.

Many Bryophytes reproduce asexually, by producing small clusters of cells called gemmae, that eventually break away and 'germinate' to form new plants. All Bryophytes reproduce sexually, producing motile male gametes (antherozoids), in delicate sac-structures called antheridia, and female gametes (ova), each contained in a flask-shaped organ called an archegonium. The archegonium has a wide, spherical body at its base and a long narrow neck. The cells in the centre of the neck break down, male gametes swim down the canal, and one of them fuses with the ovum.

The zygote develops into a spore-producing plant (sporophyte) that is dependent upon the green, gamete-producing plant (gametophyte). The sporophyte contains spores within a spherical capsule. This capsule is carried high above the gametophyte by the growth of the stalk (seta). The seta is anchored in the gemetophyte by a parasitic foot region. In its life-cycle the bryophyte shows heteromorphic alternation of generations, where the gametophyte is the dominant stage and the sporophyte is dependent upon it.

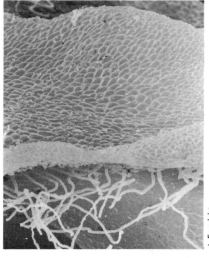

Figure 7.1 Scanning electron micrograph of part of the thallus of a liverwort, showing the simple, undifferentiated cells of the thallus, together with numerous rhizoids growing from the lower surface

J. Forsdyke

The differences between mosses and liverworts

Liverworts, e.g. *Pellia* see below *Marchantia* see p. 70	Mosses, e.g. *Funaria* see p. 71–72. *Polytrichum*, *Sphagnum* see p. 73
Rhizoids are unicellular	Rhizoids are multicellular
The plant body is usually dorsiventrally flattened into a horizontally growing, branching, and more or less ribbon-shaped thallus. (Some liverworts are 'leafy' with deeply lobed or segmented leaves attached in rows to a stem.)	Plant body is usually radially symmetrical with a central stem supporting small, spirally arranged leaves
The seta lengthens rapidly after the capsule has reached full size. The seta is a colourless, semi-transparent structure	The seta elongates slowly as capsule develops. The seta at maturity is a slender, opaque, coloured and comparatively tough stalk
The capsule contains elongated, spirally-thickened 'elaters' amongst the spores	Capsule contains no 'elaters'. The capsule is covered by a 'calyptra'

The liverwort *Pellia epiphylla*

Pellia epiphylla is abundant everywhere except where the soil is highly chalky. It can be found carpeting the soil of ditches, stream-banks or damp, peaty moorland. The thallus is dark, shiny green in the older parts but pale green at the tips. It is about one centimetre broad and branches dichotomously.

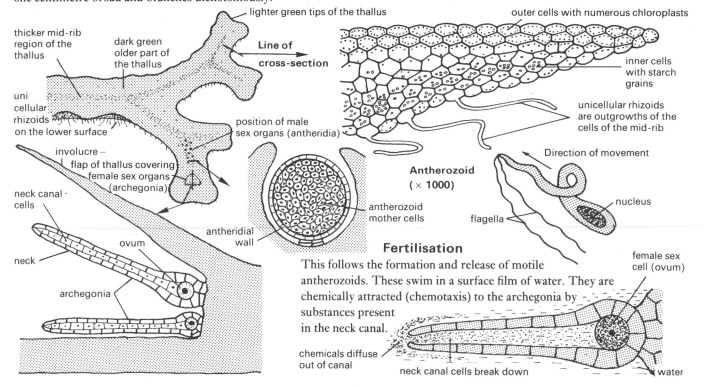

lighter green tips of the thallus

thicker mid-rib region of the thallus

dark green older part of the thallus

Line of cross-section

outer cells with numerous chloroplasts

inner cells with starch grains

uni cellular rhizoids on the lower surface

unicellular rhizoids are outgrowths of the cells of the mid-rib

position of male sex organs (antheridia)

Direction of movement

involucre – flap of thallus covering female sex organs (archegonia)

Antherozoid (× 1000)

antherozoid mother cells

nucleus

flagella

neck canal cells

antheridial wall

neck

ovum

Fertilisation

This follows the formation and release of motile antherozoids. These swim in a surface film of water. They are chemically attracted (chemotaxis) to the archegonia by substances present in the neck canal.

archegonia

female sex cell (ovum)

chemicals diffuse out of canal

neck canal cells break down

water

Development of the zygote

This occurs immediately after fertilisation, to form a dormant, over-wintering sporophyte generation, dependent upon the gametophyte generation. The zygote undergoes cell division (by mitosis) to produce a mass of cells. These cells then develop into the foot, seta and capsule of the sporophyte. The cells within the capsule divide mitotically to produce many spore mother-cells and also elater cells. The spore mother-cells finally divide meiotically to give four haploid spores. The elaters do not divide, but do elongate and lay down internal spiral thickenings. The cells of the archegonium wall also grow and form a substantial sheath of haploid cells surrounding a diploid sporophyte.

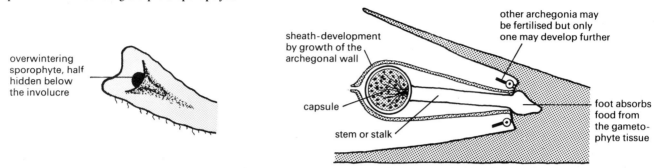

Spore release

This occurs the following spring when the seta elongates, positioning the capsule high above the thallus.

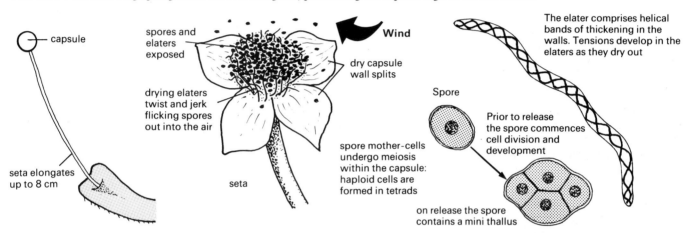

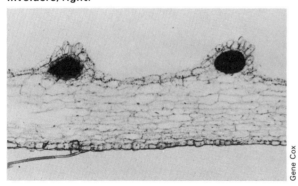

Figure 7.2 Sex-organs of *Pellia* on the thallus of the gametophyte: Antheridia, left. Archegonia below the involucre, right.

Gene Cox

Figure 7.3 Photomicrograph of a thin section through the capsule and seta of *Pellia* as it over-winters

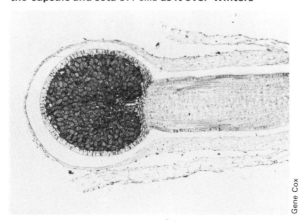

Gene Cox

Life-cycle of the liverwort *Pellia*

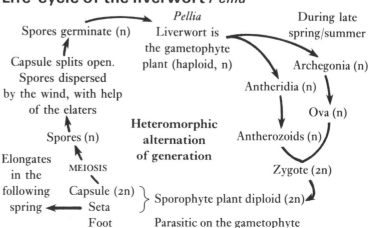

Spores germinate (n) → *Pellia* Liverwort is the gametophyte plant (haploid, n)

During late spring/summer

Archegonia (n)

Antheridia (n)

Ova (n)

Antherozoids (n)

Zygote (2n)

Capsule splits open. Spores dispersed by the wind, with help of the elaters

Spores (n)

Heteromorphic alternation of generation

Elongates in the following spring

MEIOSIS

Capsule (2n)
Seta
Foot
} Sporophyte plant diploid (2n)

Parasitic on the gametophyte

Asexual reproduction by gemmae

Many liverworts regularly reproduce asexually by means of small plates of tissue which break away and grow into new plants. These plates of tissue are called gemmae.

Figure 7.4 Gemmae of *Marchantia polymorpha* **seen on the thallus in a habitat view, and a thin section through a gemma cup**

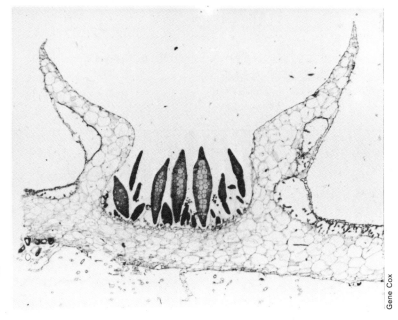

Marchantia polymorpha

This is a dioecious liverwort – male and female sex organs on separate plants. The antheridia and archegonia occur on the umbrella-like outgrowths from the thallus. After fertilisation the capsule grows down from the underside of the female umbrella.

Figure 7.5 Sexual reproduction structures of *Marchantia polymorpha*

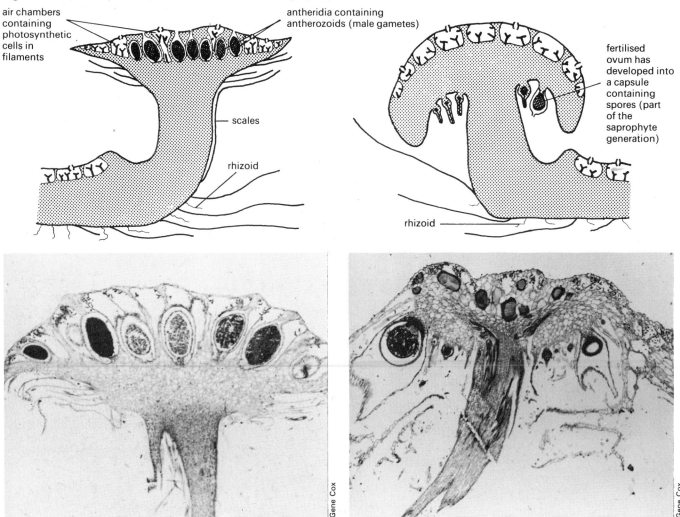

Leafy liverworts

Pellia and *Marchantia* are thallose liverworts, but the majority of UK liverworts are 'leafy'. A leafy liverwort resembles a moss, except that the leaves of the leafy liverwort are usually lobed or deeply divided, and are without the moss leaf's midrib or 'nerve'. The stem is usually prostrate and has two or three rows of leaves. Part of the leaf may be modified by folding, and form a water receptacle; for example, the water-retaining helmet-shaped pitcher of *Frullaria*.

Frullaria tamarisci grows on soil, rock or tree trunks. It is coloured reddish-olive to deep brown and the leaves have a glossy appearance. The helmet-shaped pitchers contain water and may be occupied by tiny animals (e.g. rotifers).

Figure 7.6 *Frullaria tamarisci* **shown as it grows on trees and rock in the north and west of Britain, and detail of small portions of stem, leaf and pitcher-like leaves**

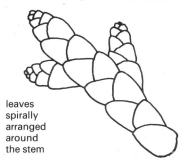

leaves spirally arranged around the stem

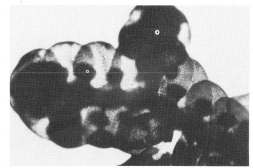

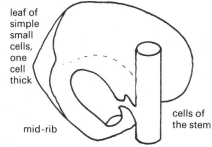

leaf of simple small cells, one cell thick

mid-rib

cells of the stem

Mosses

Mosses are more numerous and more widely distributed than liverworts. Most mosses have shoots consisting of a short, often upright stem with simple, stalkless leaves, spirally arranged. The central cells of the stem are more elongated than the outer cells. They may have a supporting and conducting role. The leaves are one-cell thick, except at the mid-rib. Mosses often grow in dense clumps or tufts, providing a humid micro-climate for themselves and for numerous invertebrates as well. This growth in clumps enables mosses to survive and grow in places that would be too dry and sunny for liverworts.

Funaria hygrometrica commonly colonises bare soil, often following a fire, and is also abundant on heathland for a year or two after a fire.

Polytrichum spp occur mostly in upland grassland or moorland habitats, usually where there is an acid soil reaction. Sometimes they occur in woodlands.

Polytrichum juniperinum is a characteristic species of acid heathland and of bare patches between heather. In natural successions this moss follows *Funaria* on burnt heathland.

Figure 7.7 A *Funaria hygrometrica* **plant**

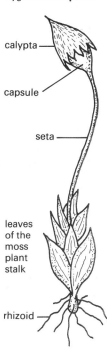

calypta

capsule

seta

leaves of the moss plant stalk

rhizoid

Figure 7.8 *Polytrichum juniperinum* **growing on acid heathland**

Chris Clegg

Figure 7.9 **Scanning electron micrograph of a moss stem cut in section, showing the simple, largely undifferentiated cells, and the leaves one cell thick at the narrow central mid-rib (× 80). Also, a drawing of a stem and leaf, seen in cross-section**

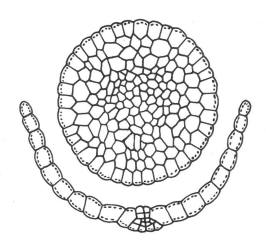

Gene Cox

Sex organs on the moss plant (gametophyte)

The moss plant produces antherozoids in antheridia and ova in archegonia. The sex organs are packed together at the top of the stem surrounded by a rosette of leaves together with numerous hairs called paraphyses. Some species have their sex organs on separate plants (dioecious), e.g. *Polytrichum*, and *Mnium*; others have their archegonia and antheridia on separate branches of the same plant (hermaphrodite, monoecious), e.g. *Funaria*.

Figure 7.10 Vertical section through the female 'inflorescence' of *Mnium* sp.

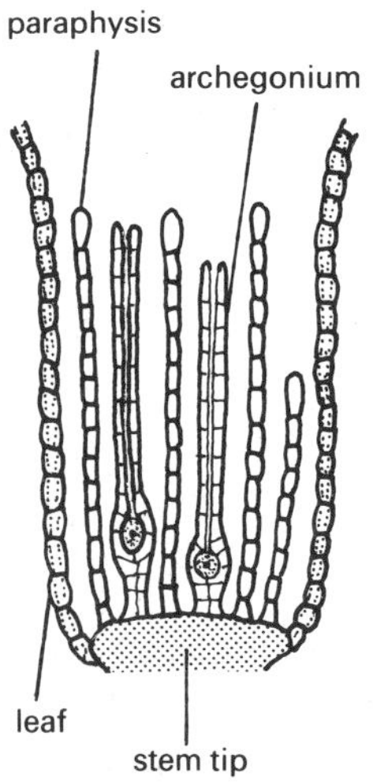
paraphysis
archegonium
leaf
stem tip

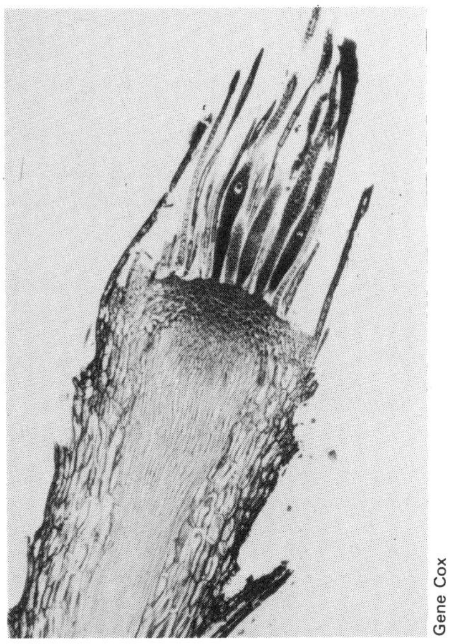
Gene Cox

Figure 7.11 Vertical section through the male 'inflorescence' of *Polytrichum* sp. Club-shaped antheridia occur packed between vegetative leaves

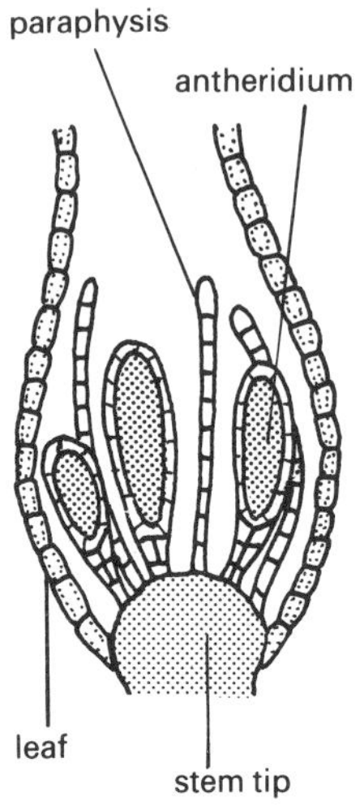
paraphysis
antheridium
leaf
stem tip

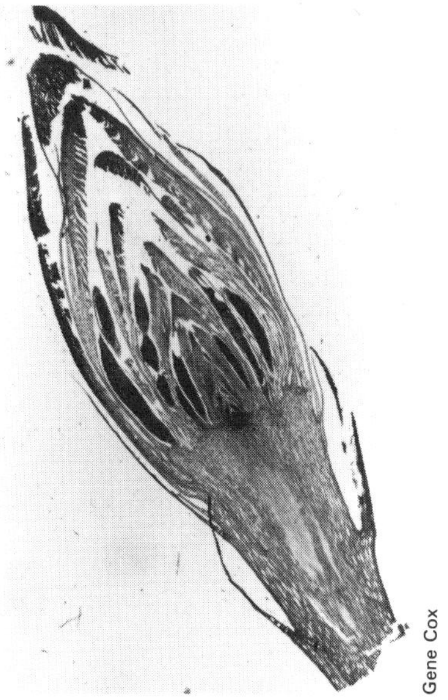
Gene Cox

Fertilisation

When the male gametes (antherozoids) have been released from the club-shaped antheridia they may swim in a surface film of moisture or be splashed by rain action to reach a female 'inflorescence'. Antherozoids swim down the neck canal. As in liverworts the antherozoids are attracted to the ovum chemotactically, and one antherozoid may fertilise the ovum.

Development of the fertilised ovum

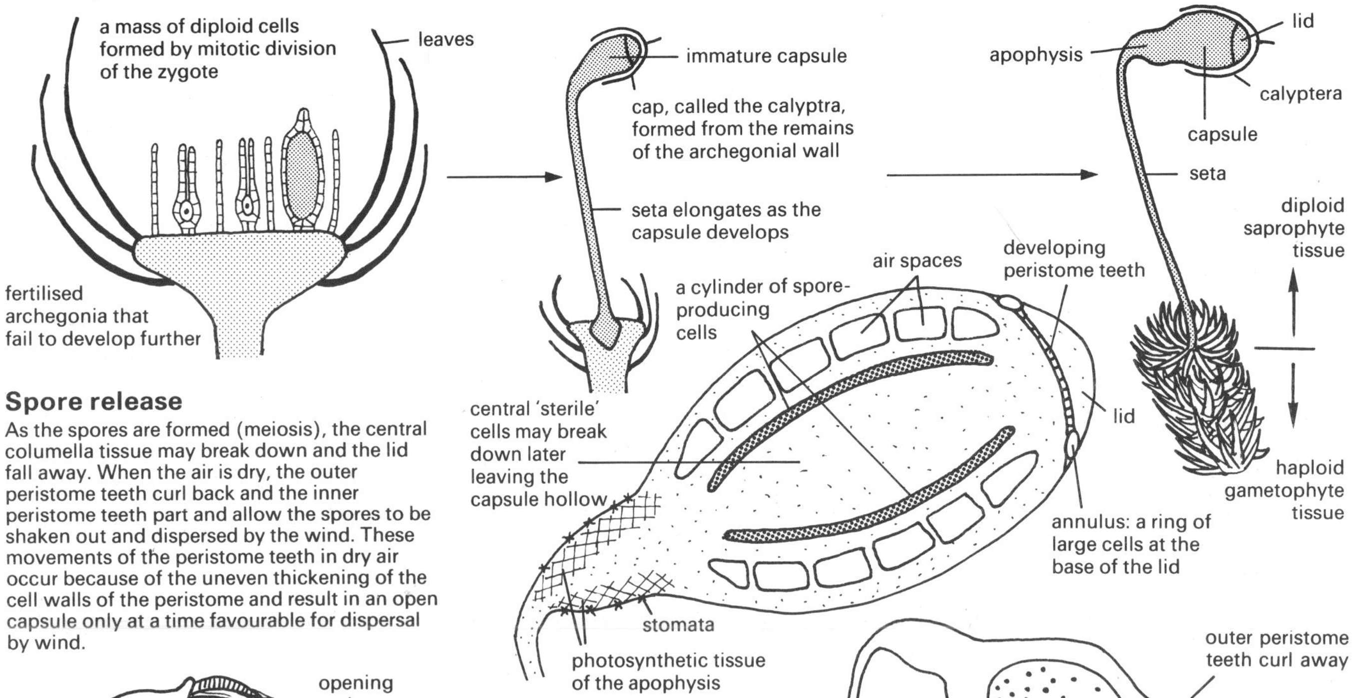
a mass of diploid cells formed by mitotic division of the zygote
leaves
fertilised archegonia that fail to develop further
immature capsule
cap, called the calyptra, formed from the remains of the archegonial wall
seta elongates as the capsule develops
apophysis
lid
calyptera
capsule
seta
diploid saprophyte tissue
haploid gametophyte tissue
air spaces
developing peristome teeth
a cylinder of spore-producing cells
central 'sterile' cells may break down later leaving the capsule hollow
lid
annulus: a ring of large cells at the base of the lid
stomata
photosynthetic tissue of the apophysis

Spore release

As the spores are formed (meiosis), the central columella tissue may break down and the lid fall away. When the air is dry, the outer peristome teeth curl back and the inner peristome teeth part and allow the spores to be shaken out and dispersed by the wind. These movements of the peristome teeth in dry air occur because of the uneven thickening of the cell walls of the peristome and result in an open capsule only at a time favourable for dispersal by wind.

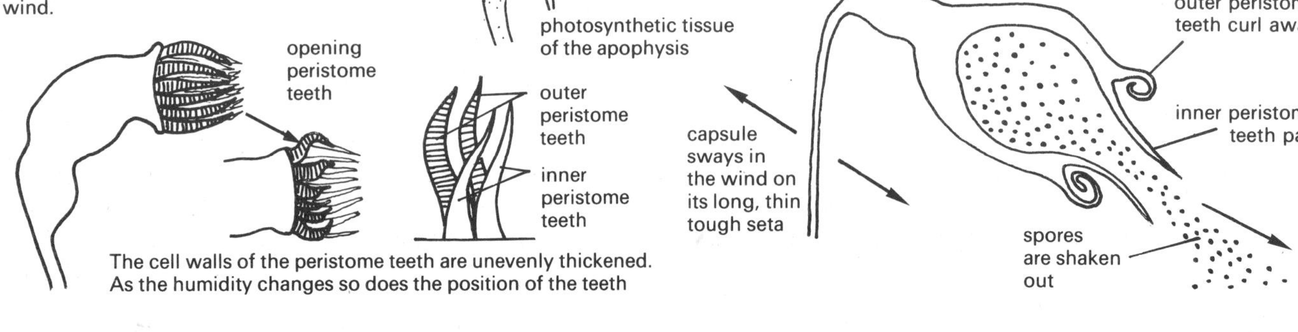
opening peristome teeth
outer peristome teeth
inner peristome teeth
capsule sways in the wind on its long, thin tough seta
outer peristome teeth curl away
inner peristome teeth part
spores are shaken out

The cell walls of the peristome teeth are unevenly thickened. As the humidity changes so does the position of the teeth

Figure 7.13 Vertical section of the capsule of the moss *Polytrichum* sp.

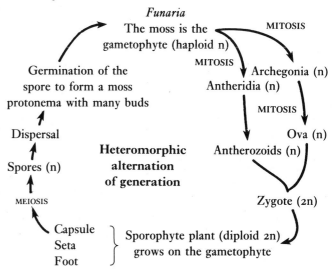

apophysis
photosynthetic
tissue

air spaces

capsule

lid

seta with elongated
central cells

region of
annulus and
peristome

epidermis
with stomata

spore-forming
tissue

central
'sterile' tissue:
the columella

Gene Cox

Spore germination

The spores germinate rapidly on damp surfaces, forming a simple green filamentous multicellular plant, very similar to a filamentous green alga. This is known as the moss protonema. Around this filament several spherical masses of cells develop, known as 'buds', and each may grow into an independent leafy moss plant.

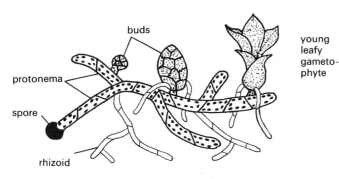

buds

protonema

spore

rhizoid

young
leafy
gameto-
phyte

Life-cycle of the moss *Funaria*

Funaria
The moss is the
gametophyte (haploid n)

MITOSIS

Germination of the
spore to form a moss
protonema with many buds

MITOSIS

Archegonia (n)
Antheridia (n)

Dispersal

MITOSIS

Ova (n)
Antherozoids (n)

Spores (n)

**Heteromorphic
alternation
of generation**

MEIOSIS

Zygote (2n)

Capsule
Seta
Foot } Sporophyte plant (diploid 2n) grows on the gametophyte

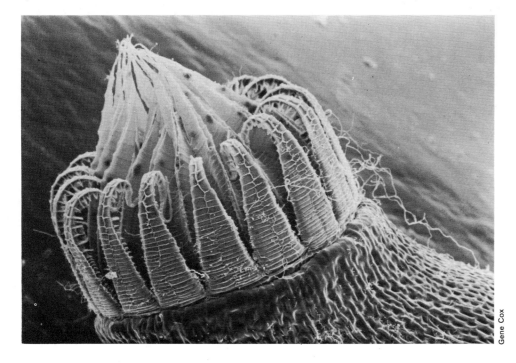

Figure 7.14 Scanning electron micrograph of the peristome teeth of a moss capsule (× 125)

Gene Cox

Moss – an ecological note

Mosses and liverworts grow on land, but they show no special adaptation to terrestrial conditions. Few of these plants can exist in really dry conditions for long periods. They are early colonisers of new habitats, following on from, or occurring with, lichens (see page 67). The absence of a waxy cuticle leaves them susceptible to desiccation and air-borne pollution.

Sphagnum mosses and bogs

Mountain areas where rainfall is high and the temperature is low are often covered with extensive 'blanket bogs'. Here mosses of the genus *Sphagnum* predominate. The leaves of *Sphagnum* contain small cells with chloroplasts arranged around larger cells (hyaline cells) with pores in their walls. These leaves retain a great quantity of water. Lakes and ponds on hills and mountains may be rapidly encroached upon by a surface community of *Sphagnum* moss, converted to a quaking bog and thence to a stable bog of wet peat.

At low temperatures and in acid conditions, decay by bacteria is inhibited and acidic plant remains accumulate. Any basic ions released are rapidly leached away by the rain and surface water. The dead remains of moss gametophytes accumulate, together with the remains of other organisms; this is known as peat.

Peat can be cut out and dried as fuel, or used on gardens as a soil additive to improve water retention and humus content.

Sphagnum cuspidatum

Ferns and their allies

Ferns are perennial land plants with the typical higher plant structures of stem, leaf and root, and a complex internal anatomy. The aerial parts of the fern are covered with a waxy cuticle on the outermost layer of the cells (epidermis). The epidermis has organised pores (stomata) that connect the extensive internal air-spaces with the outside. The fern contains water-carrying cells (xylem tracheids, see page 85). Ferns occur in many habitats, ranging from mountain-side and moorland, to walls, roofs and rock faces, and in fresh-water swamps, ditches, hedge-banks and woodland. Ferns reproduce and disperse themselves by spores and have in their life-cycle two independent stages, showing alternation of generation between the stages. In the dominant stage, the fern plant (sporophyte) bears spores. The spores germinate to form small, simple, independent green plants (gametophytes) that produce male gametes (antherozoids within an antheridium) and female gametes (ova within the flask-shaped archegonia). Fertilisation is achieved by the flagellated male gamete swimming in a surface film of water and being chemically attracted to the ovum in the archegonium. The fern is not totally independent of highly moist conditions and in this respect is not totally adapted to terrestrial life.

Common ferns include:

Bracken (*Pteridium aquilinum*), the most widespread fern, occurring all over the world. In the UK, it is common on heaths, hillsides and mountain-sides where the soil is acidic or sandy; **Male Fern** (*Dryopteris felix-mas*), very common in woodland; **Royal Fern** (*Osmunda regalis*), occurs in wet places; **Hart's Tongue Fern** (*Asplenium scolopendrium*), occurs in mixed woodland.

Male Fern (*Dryopteris felix-mas*)

The Male Fern is very common in hedge-banks, woodland, among rocks and on screes (banks of broken rock, usually found at the base of cliffs) all over the UK and temperate regions of Europe, Asia and North and South America. *Dryopteris* may become a large plant (up to 2 m in diameter) in shady, humid conditions, and it flourishes even in sunny, dry habitats. It has a short, stocky, upright perennial rhizome, with numerous roots below ground supporting a crown of leaves above ground.

Figure 8.1 Male Fern (*Dryopteris felix-mas*) growing beside a hedge-bank, in successful competition with other ferns and flowing plants

The rhizome of *Dryopteris*

The rhizome is an upright, perennial structure with the main growing point at the apex surrounded by the current year's foliage leaves. The remainder of the rhizome is sheathed by the slowly decaying leaf bases of earlier years' foliage leaves. The leaves are attached spirally. Numerous adventitious roots emerge from all over the rhizome and penetrate the surrounding soil; these roots absorb water and mineral salts from the soil.

Figure 8.2 *Dryopteris* rhizome

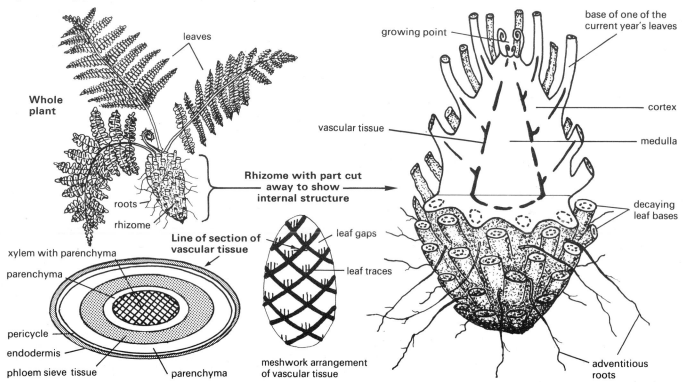

The leaf of *Dryopteris*

The leaf originates from the growing point. The young leaf is rolled circinately (from the apex to the base). The mature leaf is finely divided into pinnae bearing pinnules. Individual pinnules in section are similar to the leaves of higher plants, but differ in that they have chloroplasts in their epidermis cells.

Figure 8.3 The *Dryopteris* leaf

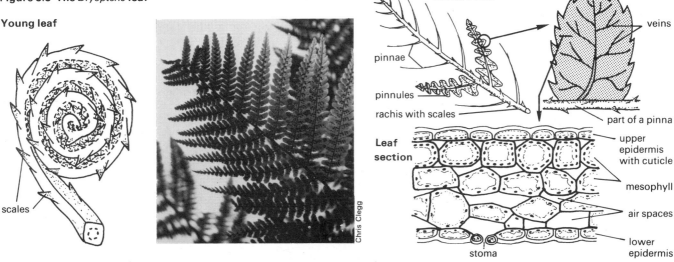

Young leaf

scales

Chris Clegg

Mature leaf

pinnae

pinnules

rachis with scales

Leaf section

veins

part of a pinna

upper epidermis with cuticle

mesophyll

air spaces

lower epidermis

stoma

Spore production in *Dryopteris*

Spores are produced in stalked sporangia on the lower (abaxial) surface of the pinnules. The sporangia occur in clusters called sori. In the fern *Dryopteris*, each sorus is covered by a kidney-shaped, scale-like cover called an indusium. When the sporangia are ready to discharge spores, the indusium withers to a smaller, brown-coloured structure, exposing the sporangia.

Figure 8.4 Part of the underside of a pinna of *Dryopteris*, showing pinnules bearing kidney-shaped indusia. Sporangia can be seen protruding around each indusium

Gene Cox

Figure 8.5 Section through two pinnae bearing sori, each covered by an indusium

Gene Cox

Figure 8.6 A sorus in cross-section, sporangium structure, and discharge and dispersal of spores

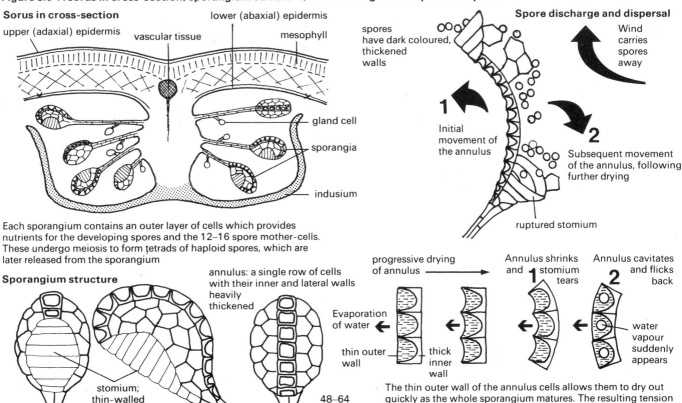

Sorus in cross-section

upper (adaxial) epidermis

vascular tissue

lower (abaxial) epidermis

mesophyll

gland cell

sporangia

indusium

Spore discharge and dispersal

spores have dark coloured, thickened walls

Wind carries spores away

1 Initial movement of the annulus

2 Subsequent movement of the annulus, following further drying

ruptured stomium

Each sporangium contains an outer layer of cells which provides nutrients for the developing spores and the 12–16 spore mother-cells. These undergo meiosis to form tetrads of haploid spores, which are later released from the sporangium

Sporangium structure

stomium; thin-walled cells, forming a line of weakness as the annulus dries out

annulus: a single row of cells with their inner and lateral walls heavily thickened

48–64 spores contained inside

stalk

progressive drying of annulus

Annulus shrinks and **1** stomium tears

Annulus cavitates and **2** flicks back

Evaporation of water

thin outer wall

thick inner wall

water vapour suddenly appears

The thin outer wall of the annulus cells allows them to dry out quickly as the whole sporangium matures. The resulting tension causes the stomium to rupture, and the annulus flicks open. Continued drying causes cavitation. The annulus snaps back. Spores are shot and shaken out by both these movements.

The germination of the spore and the formation of the gametophyte generation

The spore germinates in moist conditions, and forms a flattened heart-shaped plate of cells called a fern prothallus. This is a small green plant, completely independent of the sporophyte (fern), and it develops male reproductive organs (antheridia, each containing numerous antherozoids) and female reproductive organs (archegonia, each containing one ovum). These organs form on the underside of the prothallus and depend on a surface film of moisture for fertilisation to occur. The gametes are very similar to those of mosses and liverworts, but the antheridia have many flagella rather than the two flagella that bryophyte antherozoids possess.

Figure 8.5 Fern gametophyte (fern prothallus), showing the lower surface, and section through it showing the position and structure of gametangia

Line of section shown below

'wing', one-cell thick

'cushion', several cells thick

position of archegonia

position of antheridia

rhizoids that grow out from the cushion

cushion cells

wing cells

stalk cell

antheridium

rhizoid

developing antherozoids

ovum

archegonium

Figure 8.6 Vertical section of the prothallus of *Dryopteris*: from the cushion zone showing archegonia on the lower surface (top), from the wing zone showing antheridia on the lower surface (bottom)

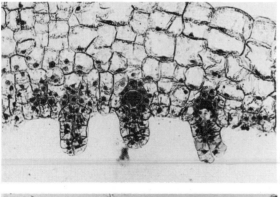

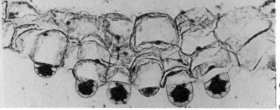

Gene Cox

Development of the zygote and the formation of the sporophyte generation

The ovum is fertilised by only one of the antherozoids that may swim down the neck canal of the archegonium. After fertilisation the zygote divides into a multicellular embryo with four regions: the foot, the root, the stem apex and the first-formed foliage leaf. As the embryo develops into a new fern plant the later-formed foliage leaves are like those of the mature fern, whereas the first-formed leaf is quite small and little divided. Initially the foot absorbs nutrients from the prothallus, but later this region and the prothallus die away.

Figure 8.7 Stages in the formation of the embryonic fern plant

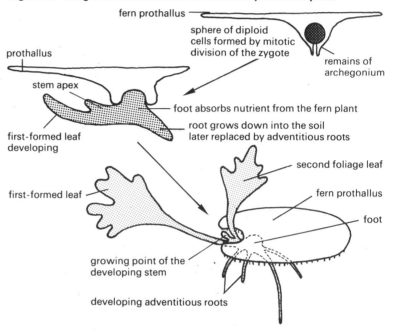

fern prothallus

sphere of diploid cells formed by mitotic division of the zygote

remains of archegonium

prothallus

stem apex

foot absorbs nutrient from the fern plant

first-formed leaf developing

root grows down into the soil later replaced by adventitious roots

first-formed leaf

second foliage leaf

fern prothallus

foot

growing point of the developing stem

developing adventitious roots

Figure 8.8 Habitat view of a fern prothallus supporting a well developed embryo with a well developed first-formed leaf

Gene Cox

Life-cycle of the fern *Dryopteris*

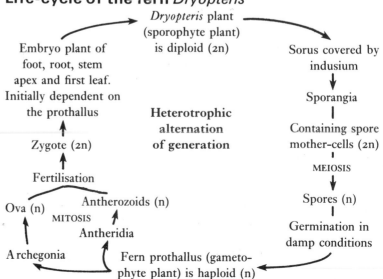

Dryopteris plant (sporophyte plant) is diploid (2n)

Embryo plant of foot, root, stem apex and first leaf. Initially dependent on the prothallus

Sorus covered by indusium

Sporangia

Containing spore mother-cells (2n)

Heterotrophic alternation of generation

MEIOSIS

Zygote (2n)

Fertilisation

Spores (n)

Ova (n)   Antherozoids (n)

MITOSIS

Antheridia

Germination in damp conditions

Archegonia   Fern prothallus (gameto-phyte plant) is haploid (n)

Bracken (*Pteridium acquilinum*)

Bracken grows on light acid soils, on heaths and mountain-sides up to an altitude of 2000 feet, and in open woodlands where it is a common dominating field-layer plant. On mountain pastures bracken has an advantage because sheep and rabbits which dominate the grazing will not eat it. On the other hand, cattle which usually dominate the grazing on lower ground may eat it fresh, and when it is cut and dried. Farmers may treat hill pastures with lime in order to kill the bracken.

Bracken has a stout, strong-growing underground rhizome which, each spring, sends up pinnate leaves from just behind the growing point. The rhizome branches and eventually the older parts of the rhizome die. In this way the plant steadily colonises new land. Bracken has a life-cycle virtually identical to *Dryopteris*; however, the sori are formed around the lower margins of the leaves (pinnules), not at the centres of the pinnules.

Figure 8.9 A bracken population encroaching hillside grassland

Figure 8.10 A bracken plant in early summer

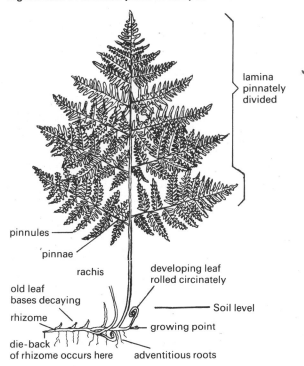

Figure 8.11 Transverse section of the sorus of bracken on the margin of the pinnule

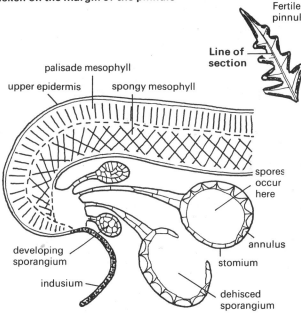

Chemical defence mechanisms in bracken

Bracken has been found to possess a number of potential chemical defence mechanisms.

1. **Allelopathy.** The capability to release chemicals into the environment which can subsequently have an adverse effect on the growth of associated plants. Such substances have been shown to come from the aerial system of bracken and from their dead and decaying remains. Chemicals may inhibit germination or growth of the seeds or young plants of other species.

2. **Phytosterols.** These are found within the leaf tissues. The two major moulting hormones of insects (ecdysome and ecdysterone) belong to this group of chemicals and have also been isolated from bracken pinnules. Their presence may confer relative immunity to insect attack by interfering with the growth processes of insect predators.

3. **Thiaminase.** This enzyme is found in bracken leaf tissue. It destroys the vitamin thiamin (B_1) in any animals which eat the shoots. Prolonged deficiency of thiamin leads to the disease beri-beri.

4. **Shikimic acid.** Leaf tissue contains this powerful carcinogen which may even keep its activity in young shoots after boiling. (In some countries they are cooked and eaten as an asparagus substitute.) This chemical causes tumours and serious haemorrhaging in animals. It is likely that cattle can transfer the toxin to others via their milk. Human populations of mountain areas, e.g. rural Wales, have shown a significantly higher incidence of stomach cancer than those of lowland Britain.

The wall as a habitat

Walls will support animal and plant communities when soil particles have accumulated in cracks and joints in sufficient quantity to retain moisture and supply nutrients for plant growth. Plants are primary colonisers and they provide food and shelter for a limited fauna. The dry-stone walls of the Pennines are built without mortar, often with hard rock. Many have remained for centuries without ferns or flowering plants; they support only lichens and some cushions or compact carpets of mosses in nooks and crannies. Other walls built with softer stone (for example, limestone or marls with a substantial quantity of calcium carbonate in the rock) and with calcareous mortar between the stones are quite quickly colonised. The normal succession of plant life is shown in the table.

Succession of wall plants

PIONEER VEGETATION	
Lichens (page 67) Bryophytes (page 69)	
VASCULAR PLANTS **Ferns**	**Flowering Plants**
Maidenhair Fern (*Adiantum capillus-veneris*)	Grasses, e.g. Wall Barley (*Hordium murinum*) Annual Meadow Grass (*Poa annua*)
Hart's Tongue (*Asplenium scolopendrium*)	Yellow Fumitory (*Corydalis lutea*) Cranesbill (*Geranium sanguineum*)
Common Polypody (*Polypodium vulgare*)	Stonecrop (*Sedum acre*) Wall Pennywort (*Umbilicus rupestris*) Willowherb (*Epilobium angustifolium*)
Rusty-back Fern (*Asplenium ceterach*)	Ivy (*Hedera helix*) Wall Lettuce (*Mycelis muralis*)

The arrival of ferns adds substantially to the biomass via the growth of rhizomes, roots and leaves, and the ferns' relatively luxuriant growth provides both substantial cover for animals and several new microhabitats. Of the animal life that visits the wall, ants and birds have an important role in introducing new plants as seeds and spores, and distributing plant material along the cracks. Visiting animal life may also add nitrogen-rich excreta.

Figure 8.12 Mortared wall with a rich flora of pioneer plants and numerous vascular plants

Chris Clegg

Figure 8.13 Examples of ferns common to walls and rock faces

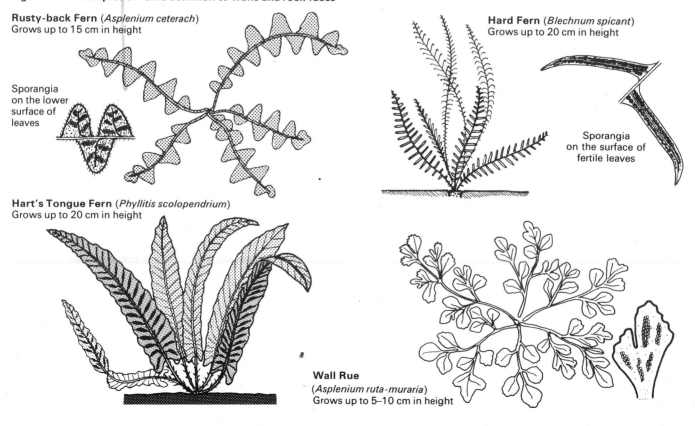

Rusty-back Fern (*Asplenium ceterach*)
Grows up to 15 cm in height

Sporangia on the lower surface of leaves

Hard Fern (*Blechnum spicant*)
Grows up to 20 cm in height

Sporangia on the surface of fertile leaves

Hart's Tongue Fern (*Phyllitis scolopendrium*)
Grows up to 20 cm in height

Wall Rue (*Asplenium ruta-muraria*)
Grows up to 5–10 cm in height

Horsetails (*Equisetum* spp)

Horsetails are wiry, ribbed and rather unusual herbaceous plants. They may grow beside ponds and streams and in marshy places (e.g. *Equisetum fluviatile* and *E. palustre*) or they may be common plants of woods and fields, growing on light soil (e.g. *E. arvense*). The plant has an underground rhizome that sends up photosynthetic stems with leaves occurring only at the nodes. These leaves are small, pointed scales growing in whorls, and the base of the whorl is fused into a sheath. Branches also occur in whorls at the nodes, growing out through the lower part of the leaf sheath. The stems are hollow and have a ring of cavities in the cortex. Between the hollow pith and the cavities of the cortex, is a ring of vascular bundles, with a similar arrangement to that of a flowering plant stem, but with xylem tracheids rather than vessels and sieve cells which lack companion cells.

In spring, spores are produced in compact cones (strobili) at the top of a stem, often on a vegetative shoot, but in some species they are produced on a special reproductive shoot that is shorter and is pinkish-brown in colour. The spores are haploid. They are thin-walled, green and short-lived. Those that survive may germinate in damp conditions and produce independent plants (prothalli) which are either male (later bearing antheridia) or female (later bearing archegonia). The male gametes (antherozoids that are multiflagellate) swim in a surface film of moisture and only one can fertilise the ovum within the archegonium. The few species of *Equisetum* to be found today are all herbaceous, and are considered to be survivors of a huge group of diverse tree ferns that grew in the 'coal forests' of the Carboniferous period, 250–300 million years ago. Horsetails are called 'fern allies', but they are not considered to be closely related to modern ferns. In fact *Equisetum* is one of the oldest surviving genera of vascular plants in the world, probably pre-dating modern ferns.

Figure 8.14 Horsetails (*Equisetum* sp.) growing at the edge of a pond (× 5)

Figure 8.15 A young *Equisetum arvense* plant, with a fertile shoot and detail of stem structure about the node

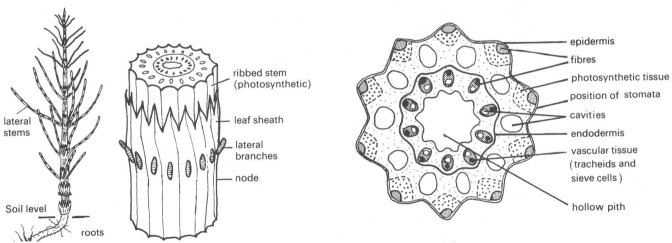

Figure 8.16 Spore production in *Esquisetum* sp.

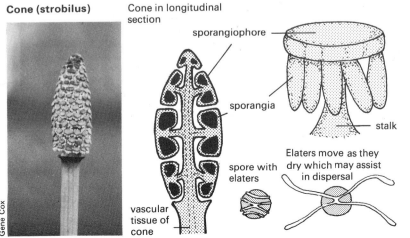

Spores seen by phase-contrast microscopy (× 600)

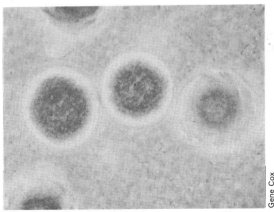

Clubmosses

Clubmosses are small, green, spore-bearing, herbaceous plants with moss-like leaves. They are found in wet heathlands and in mountainous regions, have many branches and may be either erect or found creeping. They contain vascular tissue (xylem tracheids and sieve cells) in their stems, leaves and roots. Their spores are contained in sac-like sporangia that form on the upper surface of the simple (undivided) leaves that are grouped together at the top of a stem, forming a cone or strobilus. The clubmosses have a prothallus (gametophyte) stage in their life-cycle, but it is unlike that of ferns. Clubmosses may be classified as 'fern allies' but they are not closely related to ferns. There are two main genera.

Lycopodium

Lycopodium species (there are five found in Britain) may be found on wet heathlands all over the UK, and on moors and mountains in the north growing up to an altitude of about 4000 feet.

Selaginella

Selaginella selaginoides, the only British species, grows on wet grassy or mossy ground, by streams and between rocks in mountainous areas of the north-west of Britain only.

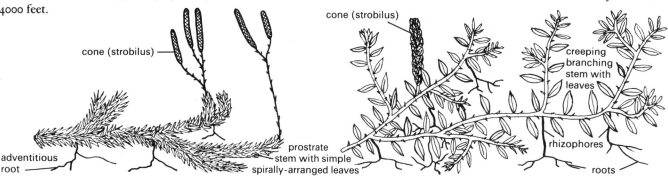

The ancient fossil clubmosses grew to be good-sized trees and they were widespread plants in the Carboniferous period. Their remains are fossilised in the coal measures that are mined as fuel today. Present day clubmosses are neither dominating plants in the habitats where they grow (although several species are abundant on, or under, the trees of tropical rain forests), nor are they of any economic significance. The interest of this group lies in the insight they give us in attempting to trace the stages in the evolution of present-day, terrestrial, seed-bearing plants.

Figure 9.1 Transverse sections of the stem and root of *Salaginella* sp. showing the vascular tissue in a central stele, similar to the arrangement in the fern rhizome

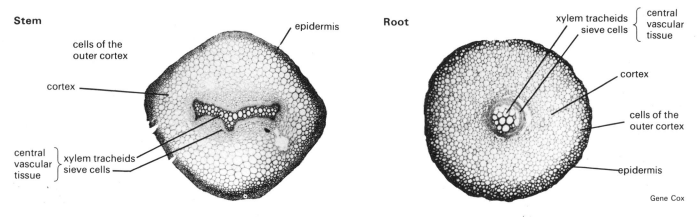

Gene Cox

Reproduction in *Selaginella* sp.

Production and dispersal of the spores

In all ferns and related plants so far described the spores are all the same. In the case of *Selaginella*, there are two kinds of spores found in different sporangia, but within the same cone.

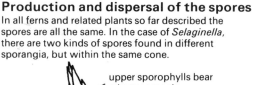

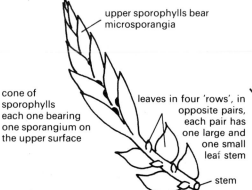

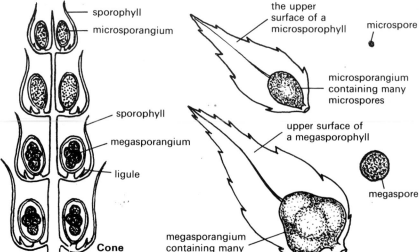

Development of the gametophyte generation

Development of the gametophytes occurs within the spore wall, as the spores lie on the ground.

Development of the microgametophyte and the production of antherozoids

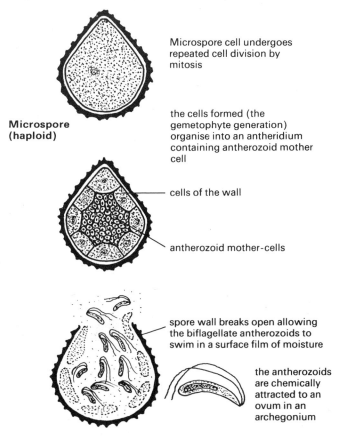

Microspore (haploid)

Microspore cell undergoes repeated cell division by mitosis

the cells formed (the gemetophyte generation) organise into an antheridium containing antherozoid mother cell

cells of the wall

antherozoid mother-cells

spore wall breaks open allowing the biflagellate antherozoids to swim in a surface film of moisture

the antherozoids are chemically attracted to an ovum in an archegonium

Development of the megagametophyte and the production of archegonia

Development commences before the spores are shed. The gametophyte formed consists of many cells

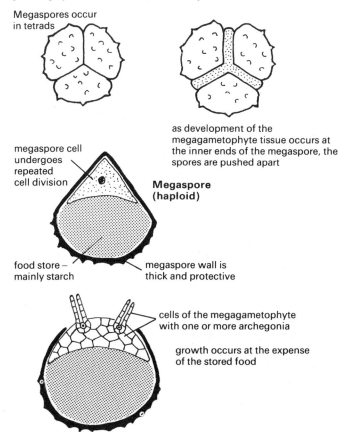

Megaspores occur in tetrads

as development of the megagametophyte tissue occurs at the inner ends of the megaspore, the spores are pushed apart

megaspore cell undergoes repeated cell division

Megaspore (haploid)

food store – mainly starch

megaspore wall is thick and protective

cells of the megagametophyte with one or more archegonia

growth occurs at the expense of the stored food

Fertilisation may occur provided microspores land close to the dispersed megaspores and if moisture is available for the antherozoids to swim in.

Development of the sporophyte generation

The zygote undergoes cell division and the cells (called the suspensor) push the developing embryo at the tip of the suspensor down into the food store. The embryo develops a stem (a growing point surrounded by leaves) a developing root, and a 'foot' organ through which the mobilised food store is absorbed into the developing sporophyte plant. The food store and the remains of the megaspore shrivel up, and the new *Selaginella* plant becomes independent.

Development of sporophyte within the megagametophyte

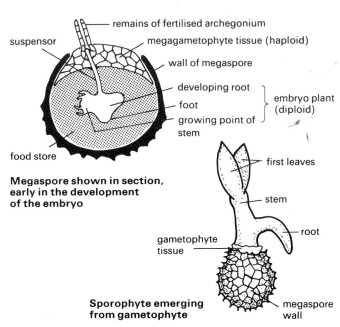

suspensor

remains of fertilised archegonium

megagametophyte tissue (haploid)

wall of megaspore

developing root
foot
growing point of stem

} embryo plant (diploid)

food store

Megaspore shown in section, early in the development of the embryo

first leaves

stem

root

gametophyte tissue

Sporophyte emerging from gametophyte

megaspore wall

Summary of the life-cycle of *Selaginella*

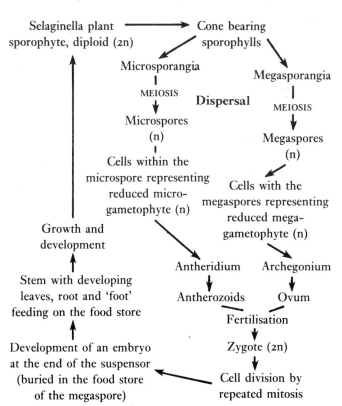

Selaginella plant sporophyte, diploid (2n) → Cone bearing sporophylls

Microsporangia

MEIOSIS

Megasporangia

MEIOSIS

Dispersal

Microspores (n)

Megaspores (n)

Cells within the microspore representing reduced micro-gametophyte (n)

Cells with the megaspores representing reduced mega-gametophyte (n)

Growth and development

Antheridium

Archegonium

Antherozoids

Ovum

Stem with developing leaves, root and 'foot' feeding on the food store

Fertilisation

Development of an embryo at the end of the suspensor (buried in the food store of the megaspore)

Zygote (2n)

Cell division by repeated mitosis

Lycopodium

Lycopodium spp occur on wet heathland throughout the UK, and are more common than *Selaginella*. They are similar in size or larger, but show several differences from *Selaginella*. The vegetative leaves are closely packed and spirally arranged on the stem. The strobili produce only one size of spore. The spores are hard-walled, resistant structures. They are slow to germinate, and may remain dormant for several seasons. Upon germination only one type of gametophyte is formed. This is a tuber-like, saucer-shaped plant that grows below ground, and it persists from one to many seasons. This survival is made possible because it lives in association with endotrophic mycorrhiza (see page 59). In addition, the gametophytes of some species have green aerial lobes which photosynthesise. Eventually the

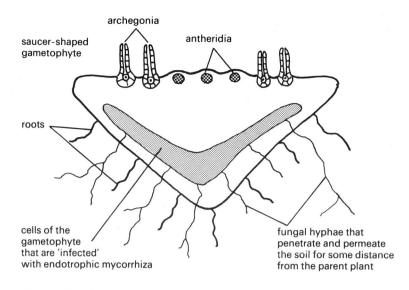

gametophyte develops both archegonia and antheridia, and after fertilisation of an ovum by a motile, biflagellate antherozoid, the zygote divides, grows and develops into a new independent sporophyte plant.

Figure 9.2 *Lycopodium* **sp. growing in grassland**

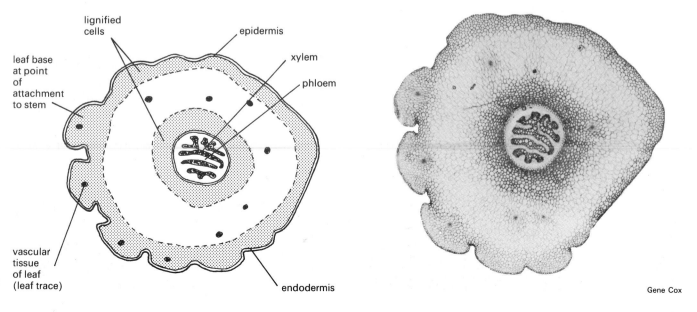

Figure 9.3 Transverse section of the stem of *Lycopodium* **sp.**

Gymnosperms

The Gymnosperms are a diverse group of seed-bearing arborescent plants with a fossil record as rich as that of the ferns and their allies. The main living representatives are the Conifers, which include pines, cedars, firs, spruce, Douglas firs, junipers, cypresses, yews, redwoods, larches and the Monkey Puzzle tree. All seed-bearing plants are fully adapted to terrestrial life. The male gamete is not a motile, flagellated cell swimming in surface water, but a cell or nucleus which is transferred to an enclosed ovum along a pollen tube. Seed-bearing plants include:

Angiosperms: the flowering plants producing seed enclosed within an ovary which becomes a fruit.

Gymnosperms: cone-bearing plants producing seeds.

The conifers are large trees usually with needle-like leaves. They are mostly evergreens. Conifers make up the dominant form of vegetation in restricted zones at certain altitudes and latitudes. They survive on many poor soils, and their association with soil fungi in the formation of mutualistic mycorrhizal roots (see page 59) has contributed to their success.

The gymnosperms are related to both the ferns (pteridophytes) and the flowering plants (angiosperms). The female ovum is contained in a structure that is recognisable as an archegonium. The microspore (pollen) contains cells that represent a suppressed gametophyte generation, i.e. retained within the microspore. The megaspore remains attached to the sporophyte plant during pollination and fertilisation. It contains cells of a suppressed gametophyte generation, i.e. retained within the megaspore. The cone itself might be interpreted as the forerunner of a flower. The production of a seed shows the gymnosperms as comparable with the angiosperms.

Figure 10.1 Natural plant life zones of the earth, and the parallel between horizontal (latitude) and vertical (altitude) distributions

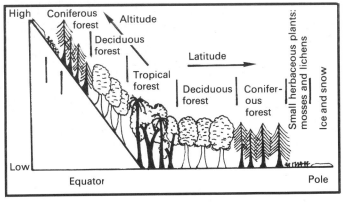

The Scots Pine (*Pinus sylvestris*)

The Scots Pine is native to the UK, and it is the dominant tree of some areas of the Highlands of Scotland. It is also found in woods in England, particularly on sandy soils. The tree grows to approximately 100 feet, and in maturity has a characteristic shape and outline, with about three-quarters of the main trunk bare of branches. As a very young tree it has a very regular, symmetrical shape. The main trunk grows straight and the terminal growing point persists from year to year (monopodial growth: growth of a stem from year to year from the same terminal growing point). On detailed examination of a shoot it can be seen that two types of branches or shoots are produced.

These are the main shoot showing unlimited growth and numerous dwarf shoots that terminate in pine needles.

Figure 10.2 Arrangement of shoots and leaves on the stem of *Pinus sylvestris*

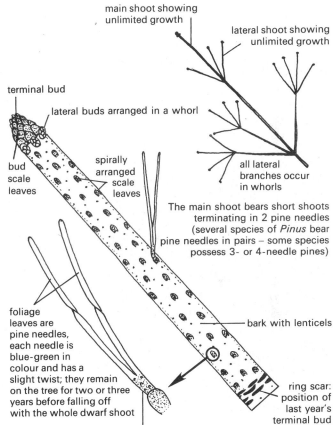

Figure 10.3 Photographs of *Pinus sylvestris* plants of increasing age

Chris Clegg

The anatomy of *Pinus sylvestris*

All conifers show secondary thickening from an early stage in the growth of the young plant. The process is the same as in angiosperm trees. A cylindrical vascular cambium (a lateral meristem) divides to form secondary xylem centripetally and secondary phloem centrifugally in the stem and root, behind the apical meristems which divide to form the primary tissues of the stem, leaf, bud and root. A cork cambium is formed in the outermost cortex and produces the bark (periderm).

Figure 10.4 Part of a two-year-old twig of *Pinus* sp. cut to show the position of the tissue of the stem, and the plane of tangential longitudinal section (TLS) and radial longitudinal section (RLS)

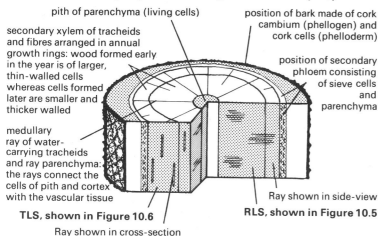

pith of parenchyma (living cells)

secondary xylem of tracheids and fibres arranged in annual growth rings: wood formed early in the year is of larger, thin-walled cells whereas cells formed later are smaller and thicker walled

position of bark made of cork cambium (phellogen) and cork cells (phelloderm)

position of secondary phloem consisting of sieve cells and parenchyma

medullary ray of water-carrying tracheids and ray parenchyma: the rays connect the cells of pith and cortex with the vascular tissue

Ray shown in side-view

TLS, shown in Figure 10.6

RLS, shown in Figure 10.5

Ray shown in cross-section

Figure 10.5 The stem of a very young *Pinus* sp. plant in transverse section (× 30)

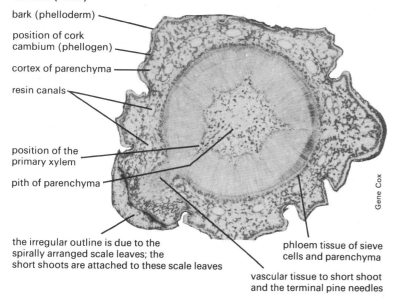

bark (phelloderm)

position of cork cambium (phellogen)

cortex of parenchyma

resin canals

position of the primary xylem

pith of parenchyma

the irregular outline is due to the spirally arranged scale leaves; the short shoots are attached to these scale leaves

phloem tissue of sieve cells and parenchyma

vascular tissue to short shoot and the terminal pine needles

Gene Cox

Figure 10.6 The stem of a three-year-old *Pinus* sp. plant seen in RLS

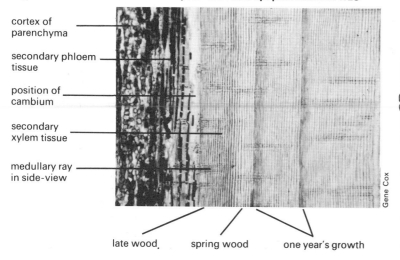

cortex of parenchyma

secondary phloem tissue

position of cambium

secondary xylem tissue

medullary ray in side-view

late wood   spring wood   one year's growth

Gene Cox

Figure 10.7 Xylem tissue of *Pinus* sp. seen in TLS (× 30). The tracheids are long hollow tubes with pointed ends. They possess bordered pits in their walls. The rays here are seen in cross-section, consisting of a single row of cells (uniseriate ray)

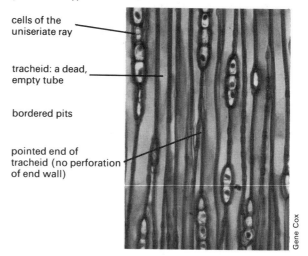

cells of the uniseriate ray

tracheid: a dead, empty tube

bordered pits

pointed end of tracheid (no perforation of end wall)

Gene Cox

Stereogram of a uniseriate ray

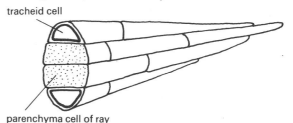

tracheid cell

parenchyma cell of ray

Xylem

These are dead, water-conducting cells with walls impregnated and strengthened by lignin. In conifers the primary and secondary xylem contains no vessels, as it does in the angiosperm vascular tissue (vessels are wider cells with end walls dissolved away to form a continuous pipe or tube). The xylem of conifers consists of tracheids and fibres. Tracheids are long, narrow cells with tapering ends. The walls are not perforated; water enters and leaves through bordered pits. The fibres are even thinner, longer and more tapered, and usually have few or no pits in the walls.

In each year's growth ring, the cells of the early-formed secondary xylem are larger, with thin walls; those of the later wood are smaller, with thicker walls. Both tracheids and fibres are non-living when mature.

Figure 10.8 The structure and function of xylem with bordered pits

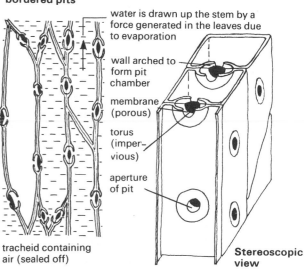

water is drawn up the stem by a force generated in the leaves due to evaporation

wall arched to form pit chamber

membrane (porous)

torus (impervious)

aperture of pit

tracheid containing air (sealed off)

Stereoscopic view

Phloem

These are living cells with cellulose cell walls, they transport dissolved food substances, e.g. sugars. The phloem tissue of conifers is simpler than that of the angiosperms. It contains sieve cells (but no companion cells), parenchyma and sometimes also fibres. The sieve cells are long, with numerous sieve areas on the walls, usually only on radial walls. Sieve areas are collections of pores that are penetrated by cytoplasm connecting the protoplasts of adjoining cells. (When these pores are large and prominent, and are collected at the ends of the cells, as in the angiosperms, they are described as sieve plates.)

Rays

Rays are cells that connect the pith, cortex and vascular tissues to the other cells. The rays are uniseriate (only one cell wide) and contain parenchyma cells which connect the pith and cortex. They are the site of lateral transport of water and food substances.

Resin canals

Resin canals are a common feature in conifers. The lumen of each tiny canal is lined by a single layer of thin-walled, unlignified secretory cells known as epithelial cells. Outside these, are one or two more layers of unlignified cells called sheath cells. Horizontal and vertical canals occur in the stem, and they may be connected into a network.

Figure 10.11 Transverse section of *Pinus* sp. root

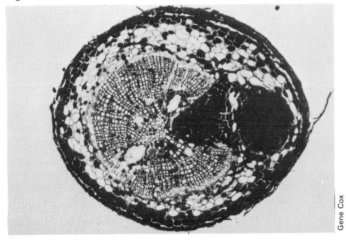

Gene Cox

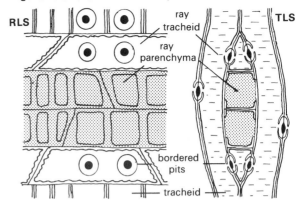

Figure 10.9 RLS and RLS of rays

RLS — ray tracheid — ray parenchyma — bordered pits — tracheid — TLS

Figure 10.10 Resin canal of *Pinus* sp. seen in a transverse section (× 30)

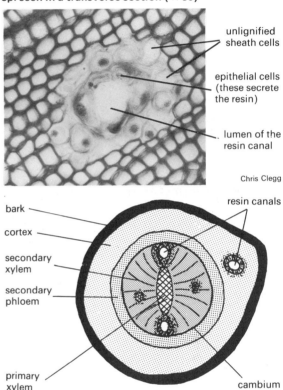

unlignified sheath cells

epithelial cells (these secrete the resin)

lumen of the resin canal

Chris Clegg

bark — cortex — secondary xylem — secondary phloem — primary xylem — resin canals — cambium

Pinus sp. leaf

The pine leaf (commonly called a needle) shows many xeromorphic features which enable it to withstand drought or a period of limited water supply. The pine needle is a compact structure with a relatively small surface area to volume ratio. The stomata are sunken and there is a waxy cuticle overlying the epidermis whose cells have very thick walls. Below the epidermis is a layer of fibres. The Scots Pine (*Pinus sylvestris*) is an evergreen tree, the needles remaining on the tree for 2–3 years. In winter the water supply may often be restricted when the land is frozen. The water conserving features of the pine leaf gives the pine tree a clear advantage in such conditions.

Figure 10.12 Transverse section of a *Pinus sylvestris* needle (× 60)

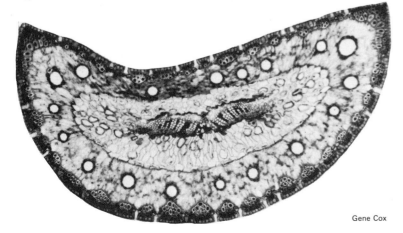

Gene Cox

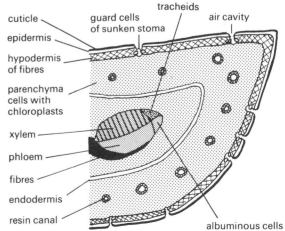

cuticle — epidermis — hypodermis of fibres — parenchyma cells with chloroplasts — xylem — phloem — fibres — endodermis — resin canal — guard cells of sunken stoma — tracheids — air cavity — albuminous cells

Reproduction in *Pinus sylvestris*

Gymnosperms reproduce by the production of seeds. In *Pinus sylvestris* the seeds are released and dispersed from female cones after three growing seasons of development.

In year one male and female cones are formed and pollination occurs.

In year two fertilisation occurs inside the female cones.

In year three formation of seed is completed and seeds are dispersed. The female cones grow larger each year. The cones that release seeds in year three are large, brown and dry when compared with the small, soft succulent and greenish female cones of year one. Seeds are dispersed by wind and the foraging action of birds and squirrels. Those seeds that survive predation germinate quickly when the moisture supply is adequate and the ambient temperature range is favourable.

Pinus sylvestris produces diclinous cones (separate male and female cones) on different parts of the same plant – the plant is known as monoecious. Both male and female cones appear in May once the terminal buds have opened and produced the new shoots which constitute that year's vegetative growth. Female cones occur near the apex of the tree and on the end of branches. Female cones take the place of lateral buds. Male cones are produced in groups on lower branches, each cone occupying the position of a short shoot (see Figure 10.13).

The male cone and pollen

Male cones are about one centimetre long, ovoid and yellow in colour. When pollen has been dispersed and the cones have shrivelled and fallen off, the long shoot remains bare in that region.

Figure 10.14 Lateral branch of *Pinus sylvestris* showing male cones clustered together at the base of the new season's vegetative growth

Howard Jay

Figure 10.15 The male cone of *Pinus sylvestris* showing pollen sacs in section

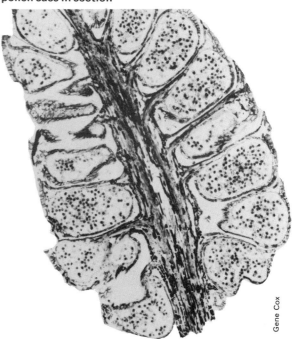

Gene Cox

Figure 10.13 Branch of *Pinus sylvestris* showing the position of male cones and a cone in LS

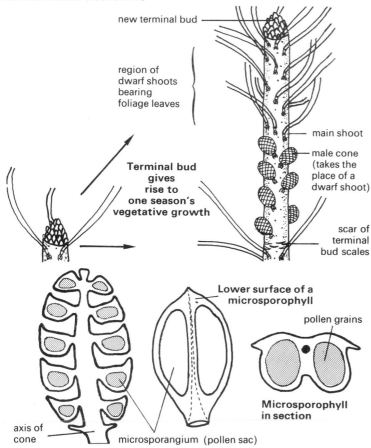

new terminal bud

region of dwarf shoots bearing foliage leaves

Terminal bud gives rise to one season's vegetative growth

main shoot

male cone (takes the place of a dwarf shoot)

scar of terminal bud scales

Lower surface of a microsporophyll

pollen grains

Microsporophyll in section

axis of cone

microsporangium (pollen sac)

Figure 10.16 Pollen grains of *Pinus sylvestris* as seen prior to release and dispersal

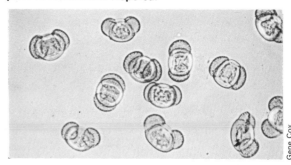

Gene Cox

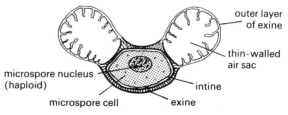

outer layer of exine

thin-walled air sac

microspore nucleus (haploid)

intine

microspore cell

exine

Immature pollen sacs are packed with microspore mother-cells (diploid). These undergo meiosis and the four haploid cells develop into pollen grains (microspores). The pollen grain has an outer wall (exine) which has a waterproof cuticle, and an inner wall (intine) surrounding the microspore cell. The pollen grain of *Pinus sylvestris* also develops two large, air-filled sacs between its two wall layers. These air sacs aid in wind dispersal. Pollen grains are released by longitudinal splitting of the microsporangia.

The female cone

Female cones are about 5 mm long, are ovoid and pinkish-green coloured. They are soft structures, clustered around the base of the terminal bud. They remain attached for three years. By their second year they are longer, larger, harder and green coloured. In the final season they have become brown and scaly pine cones. The scales part, particularly in dry weather. Pine seeds fall out and are blown away.

Figure 10.18 Position of female cones on *Pinus sylvestris*

Year one

Year two

Year three

Figure 10.17 Branch of *Pinus sylvestris* showing position of female cones

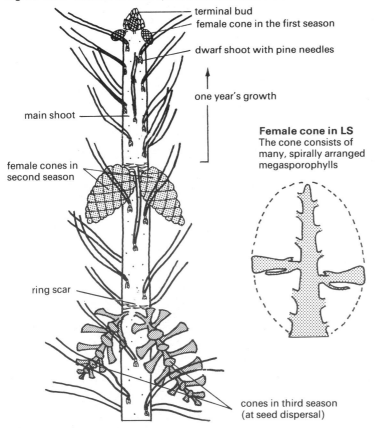

- terminal bud
- female cone in the first season
- dwarf shoot with pine needles
- one year's growth
- main shoot
- female cones in second season
- ring scar
- cones in third season (at seed dispersal)

Female cone in LS
The cone consists of many, spirally arranged megasporophylls

Development within the female cone before and after pollination

On the upper surface of each megasporophyll are two ovules, enclosed by an integument but not by an ovary. These ovules consist of a mound of cells surrounded by a sheath (the integument), except at a small pore, called the micropyle. The inner mass of cells, termed the nucellus, contains a single megaspore mother cell. Early in the first year's growth and development, this cell undergoes meiosis, and four haploid cells are formed. Three of these cells abort. The remaining cell continues to develop into the megagametophyte during the second year.

Section through the megasporophyll

micropyle
nucellus
integument
axis
bract scale
ovuliferous scale

Surface view of megasporophyll

naked ovules
micropyles
point of attachment to the axis of the cone

Meanwhile, a drop of fluid collects at the micropyle. The megasporophylls of the female cone part briefly, but sufficiently, to allow pollination to occur. Pollen grains have an opportunity to be blown in and trapped in the liquid of the micropyle. This liquid is quickly reabsorbed and the pollen grains become stuck onto the nucellus, awaiting development.

Further development of the pollen grain does not occur until about one month before they are shed from the male cones. The microspore cell in each pollen grain undergoes division in the following sequence:

$$\text{Microspore cell} \rightarrow \text{Mitosis} \rightarrow \begin{array}{c}\text{Two prothallial cells} \\ + \\ \text{antheridial cell}\end{array} \rightarrow \text{Mitosis} \rightarrow \begin{array}{c}\text{Generative cell} \\ + \\ \text{tube nucleus}\end{array}$$

This final stage is the condition of the pollen grain at pollination. We may recognise the prothallial cells as the remnants (i.e. 'suppressed' part) of the gametophyte. The antheridial cell is then interpreted as the cell of the microgametophyte that produces the male gametes.

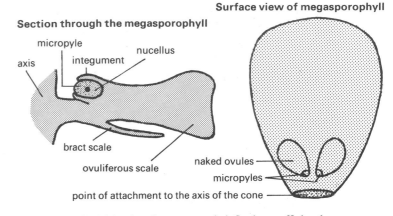

microspore
first prothallial stage
second prothallial cell
generative cell

In microsporangium — At pollination

Howard Jay

Also during the first year, surviving megaspore cell in the nucellus of each ovule undergoes repeated cell division to form a large embryo sac (we may recognise this embryo sac as the female gametophyte or megagametophyte). During the second year, archegonia develop within the embryo sacs. Meanwhile development of the pollen grain continues and a pollen tube grows through the nucellus tissue. The tube nucleus, surrounded by dense cytoplasm, moves along the developing pollen tube. The generative cell undergoes mitosis and cell division in the following sequence:

Generative cell → Mitosis → Stalk-cell + body-cell → Mitosis → Two male gametes

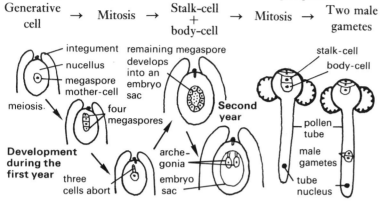

Figure 10.19 Ovule of *Pinus sylvestris* **just prior to fertilisation**

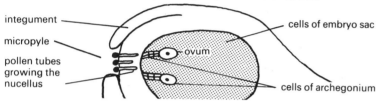

One pollen tube enters each archegonium and one of the male nuclei fuses with the ovum nucleus; the other male nucleus dies. Thus several zygotes are formed in each embryo sac.

The diploid nucleus of each zygote now passes to the inner end of the zygote and undergoes repeated mitosis. Four tiers of cells are formed and these develop into four embryos. Since each embryo sac contains two or more archegonia, eight or more embryos commence development (this condition is known as polyembryony). Only one of these embryos reaches maturity, the others disintegrate.

Figure 10.20   Structure of a seed at the time of dispersal

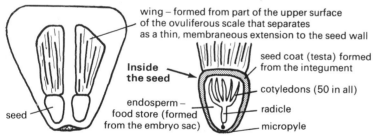

Germination

Germination may occur quite quickly after dispersal. The endosperm tissue of the seed is digested and absorbed by the cotyledons. These cotyledons also develop chlorophyll in chloroplasts in the seed, prior to their exposure to light. When the seedling is established the plumule grows to form the main stem bearing pine needles.

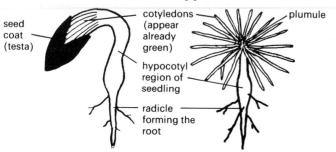

Figure 10.21   LS through the female cone of *Pinus sylvestris* **during the second year. The ovule seen in section contains large embryo sacs**

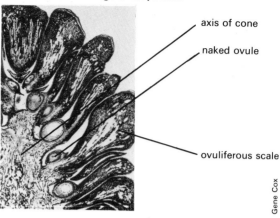

axis of cone
naked ovule
ovuliferous scale

Gene Cox

Figure 10.22   The naked ovule of *Pinus sylvestris* **seen in section. The plane of section lies just outside the mid-line, missing the micropyle**

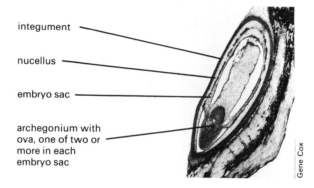

integument
nucellus
embryo sac
archegonium with ova, one of two or more in each embryo sac

Gene Cox

A summary of the life-cycle of *Pinus sylvestris*

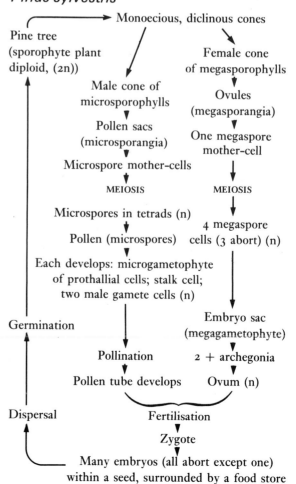

Pine tree (sporophyte plant diploid, (2n)) → Monoecious, diclinous cones

Male cone of microsporophylls
Pollen sacs (microsporangia)
Microspore mother-cells
MEIOSIS
Microspores in tetrads (n)
Pollen (microspores)
Each develops: microgametophyte of prothallial cells; stalk cell; two male gamete cells (n)

Female cone of megasporophylls
Ovules (megasporangia)
One megaspore mother-cell
MEIOSIS
4 megaspore cells (3 abort) (n)
Embryo sac (megagametophyte)
2 + archegonia
Ovum (n)

Germination
Pollination
Pollen tube develops
Fertilisation
Zygote
Many embryos (all abort except one) within a seed, surrounded by a food store
Dispersal

Yew (*Taxus baccata*)

The Yew is a native evergreeen plant of the British Isles, growing in woods and scrubland mainly on limestone. The tree grows up to 20 metres, with a massive, rust-red trunk and a rounded outline. It has a sombre appearance with dark-green leaves. The leaves are spirally arranged on the stems and are attached directly to it, i.e. no short shoots. The tree is dioecious. Male trees develop tiny cones in the period February to March, in the axils of leaves on the previous year's growth. Each cone has sterile scales at its base and fertile sporophylls above. Clouds of pollen are released. The female 'flowers' contain an ovule surrounded by scale leaves. Pollination is by wind and is followed by fertilisation and seed formation in the same year. One of the inner tiny scales grows around the seed as a fleshy cup that turns bright red. This structure is not poisonous, but the seeds and leaves are poisonous if eaten.

Figure 10.23 A Yew tree (*Taxus baccata*)

Figure 10.24 A branch from a Yew tree (*Taxus* sp.) showing vegetative leaves with the yellow male cones in the axils of the leaves

Figure 10.25 Yew tree (*Taxus* sp.) seed on the female tree. Seeds are surrounded by a fleshy red collar

Larch

The three most common species are the European Larch (*Larix decidua*), the Japanese Larch (*L. Kaempferi*) and the Hybrid Larch (*L. x eurolepis*). The larches are deciduous conifers introduced into the UK from Europe and now widely planted in forests. The wood is coarse in texture, resinous and strong, hard and durable. It is used mainly for fencing and gates. Today the European Larch is less common and slower growing than Japanese and Hybrid Larches.

Larches are dioecious and the cones appear before the foliage. The male cones are tiny, pendulous and golden-yellow. The female cones are larger, erect and coloured rose-pink.

Douglas Fir

The Douglas Fir (*Pseudotsuga menziesii*) is a large and magnificent tree, native to North America. Its wood is course in texture, fairly hard, straight-grained, resinous, strong and heavy. It is used in building construction, particularly flooring, and for fencing, pit-props, telegraph poles and paper pulp. It is a major crop in British forestry. Douglas Fir is dioecious. The male cones are yellow-brown and pendulous. The female cones which come to hang down as they develop, are pale brown with three-pronged bracts emerging between the scales.

Figure 10.26 A female Larch cone (*Larix* sp.), with vegetative bud below

Figure 10.27 Mature female cones of the Douglas Fir (*Pseudotsuga menziesii*)

Cycas

Cycas is one of a small group of plants that grow in tropical or sub-tropical regions including parts of Central America and Africa. They are gymnosperms which show strong resemblances to ferns (pteridophytes). They are thought to be related to the extinct tree-ferns (see page 91). *Cycas* is a small tree with a stout, unbranched trunk. The leaves in the crown are fern-like, in that they are pinnately divided, and the young leaves are rolled lengthwise. Unprotected ovules are borne at the margins of the megasporophylls, towards the base. Megasporophylls occur in a loose cluster, but they are not formed into a cone. Microspores (pollen grains) are produced in cones, and the development of the microgametophyte within them and the development of the pollen tube from them is quite similar to that in *Pinus* (see page 87). One exception is that the division of the body cell produces two motile male gametes. They are globular in shape with a spiral band of cilia (motile male gametes are a feature of pteridophytes rather than gymnosperms). Another exception is that the pollen tube does not grow towards the embryo sac once inside the ovule. The motile gametes are released from the tube inside the ovule and swim to the necks of the archegonia which develop inside the female gametophyte tissue.

Figure 10.28 *Cycas revoluta* which grows in tropical rain forests, and drawings of a megasporophyll and of a motile male gamete (spermatozoid)

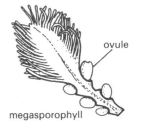

spermatozoid   megasporophyll   ovule

'Lower Plants' and the origin of flowering plants

1. The fossil record and the geological time-scale

Angiosperm fossils first occur in quantity in rocks that were laid down about 130 million years ago. By 70 million years ago angiosperms had become the dominant plant group. Knowledge about past life comes partly from comparisons of present-day living things and their geographical distribution, and partly from study of the fossil record. Only a minute proportion of the plants that existed became fossils. Fossils were formed when remains became buried with mineral particles in lakes and oceans. The sediments became cemented together and compressed into rocks over millions of years. Living remains occasionally became mineralised prior to significant decay occurring, creating an imprint or other permanent record. If subsequent movements of the Earth's surface raise up these sedimentary rocks, the layers containing fossils may be exposed by chance weathering or as a result of deliberate searches by Man. The presence of fossil remains in strata enables the history of life to be put on a likely time-scale. The existence of radioactive isotopes makes it possible to establish the age of various strata and fossils. These isotopes occur naturally in the Earth's crust, and decay to stable, non-radioactive elements at a constant rate. For example ^{238}U, an isotope of uranium, takes 4500 million years for half of its atoms in a sample to become lead (^{206}Pb). Most rock samples can be accurately dated by comparing the ratios of ^{238}U to ^{206}Pb contained in them. The results of various dating exercises indicate that the Earth, as part of the solar system, had its origin about 4600 million years ago, and that the earliest forms of life, found as fossils, appeared more than 2000 million years ago. Earth history has been divided into various Eras and these are subdivided into Periods. A geological column drawn to scale to show the relative lengths of these divisions is shown in Figure 11.1, but it remains difficult for us to comprehend the huge time-spans involved.

Figure 11.1 Geological column

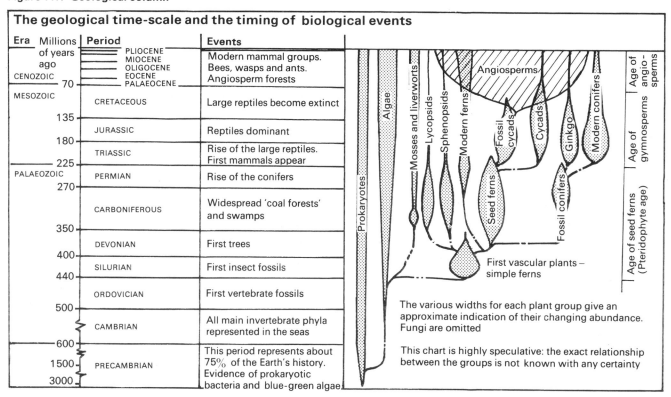

2. A theory about the origin and evolution of life

There are numerous gaps in the fossil record, yet evidence exists that allows us to postulate that animals and plants have undergone a fairly gradual series of modifications. This change in life over time, is known as evolution. Charles Darwin (1809–82) presented evidence for evolution and put forward a plausible hypothesis for the mechanism of evolution, known as 'The Origin of Species by Natural Selection'. He argued:

(a) organisms mostly produce more offspring than the environment will support;

(b) a struggle for existence results and many offspring die before reproducing;

(c) members of species are not identical but show variation;

(d) those offspring better suited to their environment have the best chance of reproducing and passing on their 'characteristics';

(e) some of their offspring will show these favourable characteristics to a greater extent, and over a long period of time natural selection of advantageous characteristics will lead to the emergence of new forms and species;

(f) offspring with characteristics least favourable for exploiting their environment are more likely to die before reaching reproductive age.

It is now supposed that life began in a relatively simple form over 3000 million years ago and by a series of many changes over millions of years, a succession of different types of living things have appeared, many of them more varied and more complex than their predecessors. Many have subsequently become extinct, but living organisms show a range, from some with closer affinity to earlier forms, to others with a greater array of newer characteristics. Taken to its logical conclusion this theory supposes that life has evolved from 'non-living' matter, possibly as outlined in Figure 3.6 on page 19.

3. Steps in the evolution of land plants

The shallow seas of early Palaeozoic times contained numerous algae, and some of these adapted to survive in sheltered terrestrial conditions. By Silurian times simple ferns like *Rhynia* possessing upright, forked branches and containing xylem and phloem tissues (i.e. tracheophytes) were common. There are no living representatives from this Period; simple ferns were extinct by the end of the Devonian. By the Carboniferous Period ferns included tree-forms growing crowded together in swamps. Altogether there were many different types of herbaceous and woody spore-bearing trachaeophytes of the sphenopsid and lycopsid forms. Sphenopsids included *Spheophyllum*, a branched, climbing plant, and giant horsetails like *Calamites*. These were similar to *Equisetum* (see page 75) in being homosporous. Lycopsids included the giant-scale tree *Lepidodendron*, with branching roots and with stem branches bearing heterosporous cones. The living *Lycopodium* and *Selaginella* (see pages 80–82) are the surviving representatives of these once dominant plants. Also in rocks from the Carboniferous Period are some fossil bryophytes and some representatives of the modern ferns with sori on leaves as seen in *Pteridium* and *Dryopteris* (see pages 74–78). But in this Period spore-bearing plants became less common than seed ferns. These seed ferns retained the megaspores on the parent plant for pollination, fertilisation, early development of the embryo and the laying down of a food store. An example was *Emplectopteris*. These advanced yet now extinct land plants must have been ancestors to both gymnosperms and angiosperms. With them and after them came fossil conifers and modern conifers and other groups now nearly extinct, including *cycads* (see page 89) and Ginkgos. Changes in climate at the end of the Carboniferous period may have been responsible for the extinction of many fern allies. The early Mesozoic era became the age of the conifers.

Figure 11.2 Examples of fossil plants

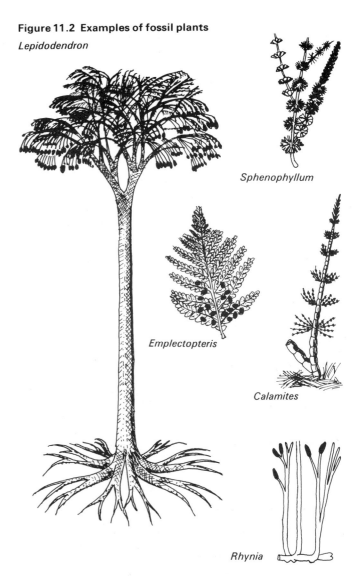

Lepidodendron

Sphenophyllum

Emplectopteris

Calamites

Rhynia

4. The mysterious origin of the flowering plants

Fossils that are indisputably angiosperms are not found in any numbers until the Lower Cretaceous. By the Upper Cretaceous angiosperms were already the dominant plants in the Earth's vegetation, with a fossil record of great diversity and advancement. The speed of establishment of angiosperms and the great rate at which they achieved diversity may be attributed to a number of features they possess that are absent from lower plants. For example:

(a) Their rapid sexual reproduction. The interval between flower production and setting of seed is usually a matter of weeks whereas in most gymnosperms the equivalent process may take at least one year.

(b) The closed ovary and the development of a style through which the pollen tubes must grow, making possible an efficient incompatability system (pollen from the same plant as the style and ovary fails to grow through to the ovule and fertilise). Incompatability mechanisms increase genetic diversity of the progeny by excluding self-fertilisation.

(c) Their unique double fertilisation. This ensures that a parent plant only invests a seed with a food store in the event of the ovum being fertilised.

(d) Their efficient vegetative metabolism and associated biochemical inventiveness in producing diverse structural and storage products, fragrant oils and unusual alkaloids.

(e) Their leaves are relatively succulent and decay rapidly after falling to the ground, producing humus from which ions are released for re-use quickly. Herbaceous epiphytes and soil-growing plants benefit from this. In contrast, gymnosperm trees (there are no herbaceous gymnosperms) have leaves (needles) that produce a slow-decaying humus that is unfavourable to the development of a diverse flora.

(f) The origin of flowers has been bound up with the evolution and development of insects. Bees do not appear in the fossil record until the Oligocene and the butterflies and moths until the Eocene. The appearance of the specialised insects can be correlated with the appearance of angiosperm families having flowers with petals fused into long tubes of irregular shapes (the gamopetalous, zygomorphic flowers of the Labiatae, Scrophulariaceae and Compositae). The evolution of the flowering plants has been a co-operative venture between insects and plants to their mutual advantage.

The origin of the angiosperms is not known. An ancestor may be found amongst the great diversity of seed ferns of the early Mesozoic Era. The ancestor is assumed to be one of these, rather than a present-day gymnosperm type. The systematic study of present-day algae, bryophytes, pteridophytes and gymnosperms reveals something of the diversity of structure, behaviour and life-cycle that plants have evolved and maintained over millions of years in response to their changing environment. The lower plants and their allies do not themselves represent a simple evolutionary sequence leading to the flowering plants.

The conservation of non-flowering plants

Introduction

The spectacular increase in human population in recent times and a corresponding increase in human activity and inventiveness is reducing natural habitats to mere fragments of their former extents. Much of the use that humans make of the land is proving to be a threat to the survival of wild life. The rate at which species become extinct has increased dramatically; it is now believed that over 2000 species of plants are threatened with extinction. For the larger organisms it is possible to identify species that are rare and endangered and to take steps to protect them. For invertebrates and lower plants the threat is equally great but these groups are less obvious and harder to protect. Throughout the world there is a movement to conserve pieces of landscape in their natural state as National Parks or Reserves, in effect, as habitat reserves. Conservation of lower plants and animals can be achieved by the conservation of habitats if accompanied by our more thoughtful and sparing use of natural resources. Conservation is not a process of hoarding and it is not automatically set against development and change. It does require the maintenance of environmental conditions and habitats to safeguard our wealth of animal and plant species.

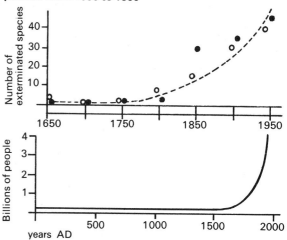

Figure 12.2 The estimated population of the world since AD 1 and, inset, the number of exterminated mammals (○) and birds (●) species in fifty year periods from 1650 to 1950

(From Spellerberg, I. F. *Ecological Evaluation for Conservation*, Arnold Studies in Biology, 133, 1981)

The major sources of threat to habitats

1. Deforestation

Trees are being cut down faster than they are replaced. Woodlands are destroyed to create space for people and land for food production. Trees are logged to release their wood and chemical resources. Forests provide wood for fuel and firewood in the developing regions of Africa, South East Asia and South America providing 58%, 42% and 20% of their respective total energy needs. This intense demand is denuding the land of trees around human communities.

Upland forests and woods are environmental buffers that make climate changes less abrupt. The trees of mountainsides (watershed forests) protect soil from erosion because they act like sponges, releasing rainwater very slowly. Without them severe flooding alternates with water shortage both on the hills and in the valleys. These extremes destroy soils, lowland habitats, and crop production. The tropical rainforests occur in South America, Africa and Asia, and are especially valuable resources for timber, pulp, fuel, fodder, fruits, game, chemicals, dyes, drugs and oils. At current rates of destruction all tropical rain-forests will be gone in less than 100 years. The particularly valuable lowland rain-forests are more accessible and are being destroyed more quickly. Within a decade these forests that are millions of years old and which support a profusion of wildlife may be permanently destroyed. It is believed that many species they contain are undescribed; their communities are approximately 50% unique to the habitat. With the disappearance of the tropical rain-forest the weather and climate of lands beyond the tropics may change. The political and economic pressures for this deforestation comes partly from the poverty and population growth of the Third World and partly to satisfy the commercial needs of Developed Countries and to maintain the supply of raw materials.

In the UK deforestation was underway hundreds of years ago, and today our countryside is open, arable land, pasture and rough grazing. Most of this land was once covered with forest. Today our hedges are an important refuge for wildlife, yet these too are disappearing rapidly. Hedges occupy approximately a third of the area of our remaining deciduous woodlands. One hundred years ago 50% of our population lived and worked on the land; today less than 1% do. We need to manage and conserve our countryside to provide for farming (80% of our landscape is owned by farmers), healthy recreation for the whole population, and to maintain our threatened wildlife and habitats. It is as important for us to preserve our remaining woodlands and hedges as it is to campaign for the preservation of forests in the Third World.

Figure 12.1 Map of the world (Peters' Projection) showing the tropical rain forest (black) and the desert areas (shaded)

Figure 12.3 The proportions of England and Wales occupied by different land use categories

(Adapted from data given in Pollard, E. Hooper, M. D., and Moore, N. W. *Hedges*, Collins New Naturalist Series, 1978)

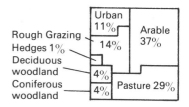

2. Loss of other habitats, and desertification

World-wide demand for new land for industrial development, transport systems and urbanisation is creating pressure for new land for food production and for greater productivity of existing agricultural land. These pressures are decreasing the habitats of every description that are available to wildlife. Over-grazing of grasslands and overcropping and incorrect use of arable land is leading to diminishing soil quality. Good land is becoming desert or semi-desert. The soils of the tropics supports lush rain-forest but only forest life, for the soil is shallow and poor and nutrients are stored in living plants. When rain-forest is converted to ranch land for cash crops it rapidly becomes useless scrub land. The rate of loss of good top-soil into the oceans as a result of all these processes is alarming.

In the UK the landscape has steadily improved in agricultural terms at the expense of wildlife. In the past 30 years the loss of deciduous woodlands is about 30%, of heathlands 60%, of wetlands 10%, and grassland by 35%.

3. Pollution

Pollution is the release of chemicals or energy into the environment by humans in quantities that damage the biosphere. Not all pollutants are waste products, some are chemicals deliberately applied to increase a particular resource, but which have an adverse side effect on other systems or organisms. Pollutants causing concern today through destructive side effects on wildlife, habitats and on humans include:

(a) Sulphur dioxide and the oxides of nitrogen, released into the atmosphere by the burning of fossil fuels. Sulphur dioxide is a very acid gas, harmful to lungs and eyes, and also to the ground hugging plants that absorb rainwater directly (see page 67). Sulphur dioxide emitted from power stations and oxides of nitrogen with sulphur dioxide released in vehicle exhaust are subsequently dissolved in rain water and shower Europe and North America with dilute acid, a phenomenon now known as 'acid rain'. Analysis of frozen snow and rain shows that precipitation has changed from nearly neutral about 200 years ago (before the Industrial Revolution) to dilute acid today. In Scotland rain falling after a prolonged dry spell has been recorded at pH 2.4, the equivalent pH of vinegar! Acid rain water reacts with and removes calcium and magnesium ions, and lowers the pH of lakes, rivers and soils. In these conditions aluminium ions, normally harmlessly bound up with organic compounds are being converted to soluble inorganic forms that are poisonous to animals and plants. Aquatic organisms are being killed, and there is now a threat to trees, to crop yields and to wild life generally.

(b) Pesticides such as the organochlorine insectides (DDT, aldrin, endrin, dieldrin). These substances persist in the environment after being applied to crops, and they remain active for up to seven years. They are fat-soluble chemicals that move through the food webs into all types of organisms and accumulate in top carnivores. A UK government statement in 1969, saying that these chemicals would be phased out of use in this country as soon as is practicable has not been heeded. In 1975–79 the use of organochlorine pesticides was 5% higher than during the period 1971–75.

(c) Lead in petrol. Lead has been used in pipes and plumbing since Roman times, and more recently it has been a paint additive. The problem with lead ions is that although they are only slowly absorbed into cells they will accumulate there to harmful levels. Since the development of the petrol engine (1910) lead ions have begun to accumulate in the biosphere. Lead combined in organic molecules (tetramethyl lead) is added to petrol as an anti-knock agent. This compound is poisonous, as are fine particles of lead and inorganic lead ions that are discharged in exhaust gases. Much of these pollutants fall to earth within a short distance of any roadway used by cars.

Concerns about the use of tetramethyl lead centre on its effects on human intelligence and behaviour, but the poisonous effect of heavy metal ions on cytoplasm of all cells should not be overlooked. A strong case has been made that lead is an unnecessary additive to petrol; changes to petrol could produce a similarly priced fuel that would be more effective in the engine and less harmful to life.

(d) Carbon dioxide concentrations in the air. Many scientist believe that the carbon dioxide concentration is increasing due to,

(i) increasing fossil fuel consumption;

(ii) tropical rain forest destruction, removing large numbers of photosynthetic plants. There is very limited evidence so far to suggest that the carbon dioxide level is permanently increasing. We are not certain what effects an increase would have. One possibility is the 'greenhouse effect' the so called phenomena when carbon dioxide accumulates and absorbs little of the incoming solar radiation and prevents some of the longer wavelengths (thermal radiation) being radiated into space. As a result the average temperature could rise and change weather patterns. The polar ice caps might melt, causing the sea level to rise disastrously. On the other hand some physicists argue that any changes in climate would be indistinguishable from natural fluctuations. They foresee that higher concentrations of carbon dioxide will also tend to stimulate photosynthesis, and so increase crop productivity. This divergence of opinion is becoming more acute, at the present time rather than being resolved.

Human life-styles; the heart of the problem

Planet Earth's capacity to support people and wild life is threatened by human activities. This threat is occurring at a time when the size of the human population is growing fast. The facts seem to show that a quarter of the world's population is consuming two thirds of the world's resources, while a further half of the population is struggling merely to stay alive and as a result, the ecological systems, upon which all life depends, are being destroyed. The main obstacles to a solution for this ecological crisis are many and complex, but they include:

(a) the belief that conservation is a specialised activity that should be implemented in a distant country by someone else;

(b) the failure to integrate conservation with productivity or development;

(c) the lack of support for conservation because of lack of awareness of the crisis that is developing.

If the current rate of land degradation continues, about one third of the world's arable land will be destroyed in the next 20 years. In a similar period, about half of the remaining tropical forests will have been logged and cleared, and the world's population is expected to increase by almost half, from just over 4000 million to just under 6000 million. Within this scenario the destruction of a great variety of habitats and the great diversity of living things could go hand in hand with the destruction of ourselves.

Figure 12.4 The pH scale and the pH of some common substances

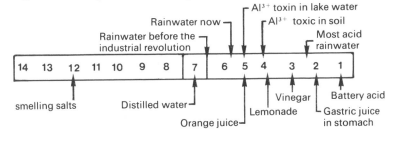

Figure 12.5 The disproportionate consumption of resources by the affluent Developed Countries compared to the poorer Third World Countries

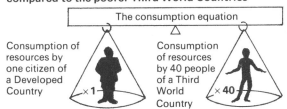

Glossary
The following are explanations and reminders rather than formal definitions.

antherozoid a motile male gamete formed in an organ called an antheridium

antibiotic a substance (usually produced by a living organism) which, in low concentration, inhibits the growth of other organisms

antibodies chemicals made by the body in response to parasites or to foreign substances called antigens. These chemicals neutralise the antigens

archegonium a flask-shaped, multicellular female sex organ characteristic of liverworts, mosses and ferns

attenuate to reduce the virulence of a pathogenic organism

autolysis self-digestion of the body within an organism that has just died

autoradiograph a photographic image produced by rays from a radioactive source

autospores a spore that has the same form as the parent cell

autotroph self-nourishing organism, capable of synthesising food from inorganic compounds

auxospore a spore formed by some diatoms, by the fusion of two protoplasts

binomial system a system of naming organism with two names, the first being the genus, the second the species

cellular composed of cells

cellulose a carbohydrate made of glucose units condensed together (a polysaccharide) in long fibres. Chief component of plant cell walls

centrifugal from centre to outside. Centripetal, from outside to centre

chitin the main structural material in the exoskeleton of the insects (arthropods). A nitrogenous polysaccharide

chromatography a technique for separating and identifying components of chemical mixtures

coenocytic a multinucleate plant body; cell walls are absent between nuclei

commensal two unrelated organisms living in close association, in which the smaller commensal derives benefits from a larger host which is unharmed

conceptacles cavities in the thallus of certain seaweeds in which the gametangia may develop

conidium an asexual spore produced by certain fungi, usually formed at the tips of specialised hyphae called conidiophores (*pl.* conidia)

conjugation the joining together of two individuals in which there is a transfer of nuclear material from one cell to the other

contractile vacuole excretory organelle, present in certain protista, which fills with fluid and then discharges its contents through the cell membrane

coprophilous feeding on dung

crustose lying flat, closely attached to the substrate

cytoplasmic streaming movement of the semi-fluid substance of the cell

dioecious having male and female sex organs on separate individuals

electron a constituent of the atom, visualised as a particle orbiting the nucleus, or as a cloud of negative charge

endoplasmic reticulum a system of fluid filled, branching tubules in the cytoplasm of the cell

endospore a thick-walled spore formed within a parent cell

endotoxin a toxin produced by a bacterial cell which is released after death and disintegration of bacterium. Exotoxins diffuse from the living cell

engulf to 'swallow' or surround and take into the body in a food vacuole

epiphyte a plant growing attached to another, but is not parasitic upon it

eukaryote an organism in which the nucleus is enclosed in a distinct membraneous envelope

faculative aerobe/anaerobe able to respire aerobically or anaerobically when necessary (an obligate aerobe can respire only in air)

foliose having a leafy plant body

fruticose shrub-like, e.g. an erect, branched lichen

gamete a sex cell (haploid)

genus a sub-division of a family which includes one or more closely related species

glycogen a polysaccharide food reserve usually found in animal cells

grana stacks of disc-shaped membranes inside the chloroplast where the photosynthetic pigments are housed, and where the 'light reaction' occurs.

haemocytometer a special microscope slide used for counting blood cells

hapteron a root-like holdfast formed by some brown algae which attaches the thallus to rock

haustorium an organ found in parasitic plants which penetrates host cells, and digests/absorbs their contents

hemicellulose a polysaccharide, similar to cellulose but more soluble

herbaceous plant a non-woody plant

hermaphrodite organism that possesses both male and female gametangia

heterotroph an organism that feeds on other organisms or their products

holdfast an organ of attachment, for anchorage

hyphae the fine tubes of the body (mycelium) of a fungus

immunisation the process of becoming immune to infection

incompatibility the failure of pollen to successfully produce a pollen tube and fertilise an ovule when on the stigma of a flower

integument of seed plants; layer(s) surrounding the ovule nucellus

isogamous all the gametes are the same size and form. Oogamous gametes are of unequal size, such as a small, motile male gamete and a larger, non-motile female gamete

leucocyte a type of white blood cell

lignin a substance present in the walls of woody plant cells with cellulose, making them tough and woody

lysis the destruction and dissolution of cells by enzymes

lysozyme an antibacterial enzyme present in tears, nasal secretions, etc

medullary ray a sheet of mainly living cells extending radially from the xylem to the phloem in woody stems

mitochondria organelles found in the cytoplasm of cells, concerned with respiration, often rod-like, but may be almost any shape

monoecious having both male and female gametangia on the same individual, e.g. antheridial and archegonial cups on the same moss, or male and female cones on the same pine tree (literally 'one body')

mutation a sudden change in the characteristics of an organism which is capable of being transmitted to offspring

mutualism organisms living together to their mutual advantage

mycorrhiza a mutualistic relationship between soil-inhabiting fungi and the roots of trees or other plants

nodule a small rounded mass, e.g. those on the roots of many Legumes

nucleic acid one of the organic compounds in the nucleus which controls the activity of the cell

nucellus in seed-bearing plants, the tissue that surrounds the embryo sac

obligate anaerobe an organism that can respire only in the absence of air

oogonium a single-celled organ or structure in algae or fungi which produces the female gamete

organelle a specialised structure which performs a definite function in a cell, e.g. mitochondria often surrounded by a membrane

ovum a female sex cell

pasteurisation treatment of milk, juices and beer by heating, but not boiling, to destroy unwanted micro-organisms

phagocyte a cell with the ability to engulf particles, certain white blood cells

phelloderm the inner layer of the bark of the tree

phosphoglyceraldehyde (PGA) a three-carbon sugar residue; an intermediate in photosynthesis and in respiration

phospholipid a compound formed of fat and phosphoric acid. A component of cell membranes

phycobiont the algal component in a lichen (the fungal component is called the *mycobiont*)

plankton very small aquatic organisms of freshwater and seawater that float passively or move only slowly in the water

plasmalemma the plasma membrane or cell membrane

precursor a substance which is transformed into a more complex metabolite

producer an organism, e.g. a green plant, which can manufacture organic compounds from simple inorganic substances

prokaryote cells (bacterial, blue-green algae) in which the nucleus is not separated from the cytoplasm by a nuclear membrane, and the hereditary material is not organised into chromosomes

protista a major taxonomic group of eukaryotic and single-celled organisms

radioactive labelling the incorporation of radioactive isotopes in metabolites to investigate the biochemical pathways of metabolism

raphe a longitudinal groove in the valve (cell wall) of a diatom

ribosome organelle found in cytoplasm of cells; site of protein synthesis

ribulose diphosphate a five-carbon sugar, the acceptor molecule for CO_2 in photosynthesis

rhizome a stem that grows horizontally, producing branches and roots

saprophyte a plant that obtains its nourishment directly from dead organic matter

secondary thickening formation of additional, secondary vascular tissue by activity of cambium cells, with accompanying increase in diameter of stem

sine wave a wave form as seen in the motion of some flagella

single-cell protein protein extracted from bacteria, algae or fungi and used as human or animal feed

soredium an asexual reproductive structure of lichens, consisting of a group of algal cells enclosed with some fungal hyphae

soralium a specialised part of a lichen thallus producing soredium

species a basic taxonomic grouping (a division of a genus). A group of individuals of common ancestry with numerous common features, able to breed together and produce fertile offspring

spectrophotometer an instrument for measuring the intensity and wavelength of light, used in chemical analysis

sporangium a specialised structure in which spores are produced

sporangiophore a stalk-like structure in fungi with sporangia at the tip

stroma the loose network of membranes around the grana. Site of the 'dark' reactions of photosynthesis

taxonomy the science of classification

toxoid a toxin which has been modified so that toxic properties are lost

tracheid in vascular plants; a dead, elongated cell, with a cavity. Its function is support and water transport

uniseriate ray a medullary ray made of a single layer of cells

unisexual male or female only

UV radiation (ultra-violet), short wavelength light, between blue and X-rays

vaccine a preparation of dead, inactivated or harmless bacteria or viruses, which when injected into the body cause the production of antibodies

virus an ultramicroscopic particle that may live in cells of plants or animals and cause disease

volutin granules of nucleic acid and related substances present in yeast and certain bacteria

Classification

The classification of plants and animals used in this book is based on Leedale's Four Kingdom System, shown in outline in Figure 1.1 on page 4. The protista are shown as a level of organisation, not as a separate kingdom. The term division is similar to phylum used in the classification of animals.

The problems in achieving an agreed classification can be perceived by comparing the schemes proposed and the arguments presented in the following references.

Hutchinson, C. S., 'Biological Classification', in *School Science Review 61 . 215*, December 1979, pp 239–246

Rushton, B. S., 'An Expanded Classification of the Plant Kingdom', in *School Science Review 62 . 221*, June 1981, pp 648–654

Holmes, S., *Outline of Plant Classification*, Longman, 1983

Further reading

CELL ULTRASTRUCTURE
Dodge, J. D. *An Atlas of Biological Ultrastructure*, Edward Arnold, 1968
Grimstone, A. V. *The Electron Microscope in Biology*, Studies in Biology no. 9. Edward Arnold, 1977

BACTERIA
Brierley, C. L. 'Microbiological Mining', *Scientific American*, August 1982, pp. 47–51
Clegg, A. G. & Clegg, P. C. *Man against Disease*, Heinemann, 1973
Humphries, J. *Bacteriology*, John Murray 1974
Volk, W. A. & Wheeler, M. F. *Basic Microbiology*, Lippincott, 1980

BLUE-GREEN ALGAE
Fay, P. *The Blue-Greens*, Studies in Biology, no. 160. Edward Arnold, 1984
Postgate, J. *Nitrogen Fixation*, Studies in Biology no. 92. Edward Arnold, 1978

ALGAE
Ovenden, D. & Barrett, J. *Collins Handguide to the Sea Coast*, Collins, 1981

Hall, D. O. & Rao, K. K. *Photosynthesis*, Studies in Biology no. 37. Edward Arnold, 1972
Round, F. E. *The Biology of the Algae*, Edward Arnold, 1973

FUNGI
Ashworth, J. M. & Rose, F. *The Biology of Slime Moulds*, Studies in Biology no. 56. Edward Arnold, 1975
Deverall, B. J. *Fungal Parasitism*, Studies in Biology no. 17. Edward Arnold, 1981
Harley, J. L. *Mycorrhiza*, Carolina Biology Reader, 1971
Berry, D. R. *The Biology of Yeasts*, Studies in Biology no. 140. Edward Arnold, 1982
Hudson, H. J. *Fungal Saprophytism*, Studies in Biology no. 32. Edward Arnold, 1980
Ingold, C. T. *The Biology of Fungi*, Hutchinson, 1972
Ingold, C. T. *The Biology of Mucor and its Allies*, Studies in Biology no. 88. Edward Arnold, 1978
Ingold, C. T. *The Nature of Toadstools*, Studies in Biology no. 113. Edward Arnold, 1979
Mitchell, D. 'The Bark Myxomycetes: their collection, culture and identification', *School Science Review* 59. 204. pp. 444–455 March, 1977

Phillips, R. *Mushrooms and other Fungi of Great Britain and Europe*, Pan, 1981

LICHENS
Hawksworth, D. L. & Rose, F. *Lichens as Pollution Monitors*, Studies in Biology no. 66. Edward Arnold, 1976
Hale, M. E. *The Biology of Lichens*, Edward Arnold, 1974
Kershaw, K. A. & Alvin, K. L. *The Observer's Book of Lichens*, Warne, 1979

BRYOPHYTES
Brightman, F. H. *The Oxford Book of Flowerless Plants*, Oxford, 1979
Watson, E. V. *Mosses*, Carolina Biology Reader, 1972
Watson, E. V. *British Mosses and Liverworts*, Cambridge University Press, 1960

FERNS
Bell, P. & Woodcock, C. *The Diversity of Green Plants*, Edward Arnold, 1971
Botanical Journal of the Linnean Society. *The Biology of Bracken*, Vol. 73, 1–3. Academic Press, 1976
Phillips, R. *Grasses, Ferns, Mosses and Lichens of Great Britain*, Pan, 1980

GYMNOSPERMS
Forestry Commission. *Know Your Conifers*, HMSO, 1970

INDEX